WOODWORK
Designing, Constructions and Workshop Practice

J. MAYNARD   Former Principal Lecturer in Design Technology, Shoreditch College; Examiner for G.C.E. Examinations at Ordinary and Advanced Levels

D. A. JONES   Adviser in Craft and Design for Bradford Metropolitan Council

HULTON EDUCATIONAL PUBLICATIONS

FOREWORD

This book has been written to help the young craftsman solve design and interrelated constructional problems. Practically the whole of the subject matter has been presented in the form of annotated sketches, and this pictorial form in addition to the comprehensive Index enables the reader to solve his problems easily and quickly at either the drawing board or the bench.

It is hoped that boys engaged on individual projects in the School Workshop will be encouraged to find out information for themselves, thus becoming more self-reliant and confident. As a result their work should proceed more smoothly, and the Craft Master will be relieved of some of the heavy pressure exerted on him when classes are covering a wide range of work.

It has been assumed that much of the basic work covered in the book on *Craft Practice in Wood* will already be familiar to the reader, and therefore the aim of this book has been to cover the principles underlying various aspects of the craft and then to relate them to specific forms of construction. Only where particular difficulty might be experienced has detailed procedure been given. The range of the work has been kept as wide as possible, and varies from the simplest form of construction to that required for 'A' level and beyond.

It would be more than presumptuous to suggest that the methods outlined in the following pages were the only ones, but experience has shown them to be both practical and successful. Where possible a number of solutions have been offered so that the reader is free to choose that one which is most suitable for the particular job in hand.

The authors are greatly indebted to many colleagues and friends who have helped and encouraged them in both the production and revision of this book; and especially to those who willingly allowed them to use examples of their work to illustrate points in the text. Finally they would like to express grateful thanks to Mr. Les Ouseley and Mr. Tony Leigh for taking the photographs used in the script.

CONTENTS

DESIGN PROCEDURE

GENERAL CONSIDERATIONS

1. **THE PROBLEM** —— THIS SHOULD BE STATED CLEARLY AND IN CONCISE TERMS.

2. **ANALYSIS AND RESEARCH** POSSIBILITIES — RANGE, PRICE, DIFFICULTY.

    FITNESS FOR PURPOSE —— EITHER FROM A PRACTICAL POINT OF VIEW OR AN APPEAL TO THE VISUAL SENSE.

    AESTHETIC APPEAL —— MUST ARISE OUT OF THE JOB AND ITS ULTIMATE SETTING AND USE.

    SIZES —— SHOULD BEAR SOME RELATIONSHIP TO MANUFACTURERS' STOCKS AND AVAILABILITY.

    CHOICE OF MATERIALS —— COLOUR AND TEXTURE ARE IMPORTANT FACTORS. AVOID THE MIXING OF TOO MANY MATERIALS.

    CONSTRUCTION —— SHOULD ARISE NATURALLY OUT OF WELL TRIED AND PROVEN METHODS. SIMPLE SOLUTIONS TO CONSTRUCTIONAL PROBLEMS ARE OFTEN THE BEST, BUT ADVANTAGE SHOULD BE TAKEN OF MODERN METHODS WHEN POSSIBLE.

3. **PRELIMINARY SKETCHES** — AT THIS STAGE VISUAL IDEAS BEGIN TO TAKE SHAPE.

4. **ORTHOGRAPHIC SCALE DRGS.** —— ON THE DRAWING BOARD PROPORTION, FORM, AND SIZE ARE WORKED OUT WITH CARE AND PRECISION.

5. **SCALE MODEL** — BASED ON NO. 4 THIS PROVIDES A THREE DIMENSIONAL VIEW OF THE JOB THE GENERAL EFFECT CAN NOW BE ASSESSED AND AMENDMENTS MADE WHERE NECESSARY.

6. **WORKING DRAWINGS** —— DRAWN TO THE LARGEST POSSIBLE SCALE ALL CONSTRUCTIONAL PROBLEMS ARE NOW WORKED OUT AND FULL SIZE DETAILS MADE OF ALL JOINTS.

7. **MATERIALS LIST** — THIS IS COMPILED FROM NO. 6.

8. **WORKSHOP PROCEDURE** —— A LOGICAL PROCEDURE SHEET MAY NOW BE DRAWN UP TO ESTABLISH A PRACTICAL ORDER OF WORK AT THE BENCH.

9. **PRODUCTION OF THE FINAL SOLUTION** —— REMEMBER THAT AMENDMENTS MAY BE MADE EVEN AT THIS STAGE.

10. **VALIDATION** —— ON COMPLETION OF THE JOB EVALUATE AND CONSTRUCTIVELY CRITICIZE THE FINISHED PRODUCT AND THE METHODS USED.

POSSIBLE SOLUTIONS TO PROBLEMS ARE DEVELOPED OVER THE NEXT 17 PAGES.

DESIGN BRIEF/PROBLEM — TO PROVIDE A SMALL WORKING SURFACE FOR REFRESHMENTS AND A STORAGE SPACE FOR MAGAZINES. IT IS TO TAKE THE FORM OF AN OCCASIONAL TABLE SUITABLE FOR USE IN AN AVERAGE SIZED LOUNGE

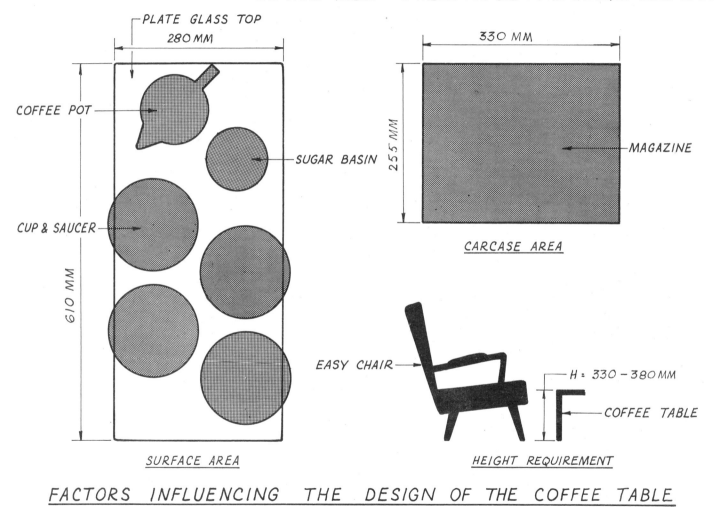

PLATE GLASS TOP

280 MM

COFFEE POT

SUGAR BASIN

CUP & SAUCER

610 MM

SURFACE AREA

330 MM

25.5 MM

MAGAZINE

CARCASE AREA

EASY CHAIR

H = 330 – 380 MM

COFFEE TABLE

HEIGHT REQUIREMENT

FACTORS INFLUENCING THE DESIGN OF THE COFFEE TABLE

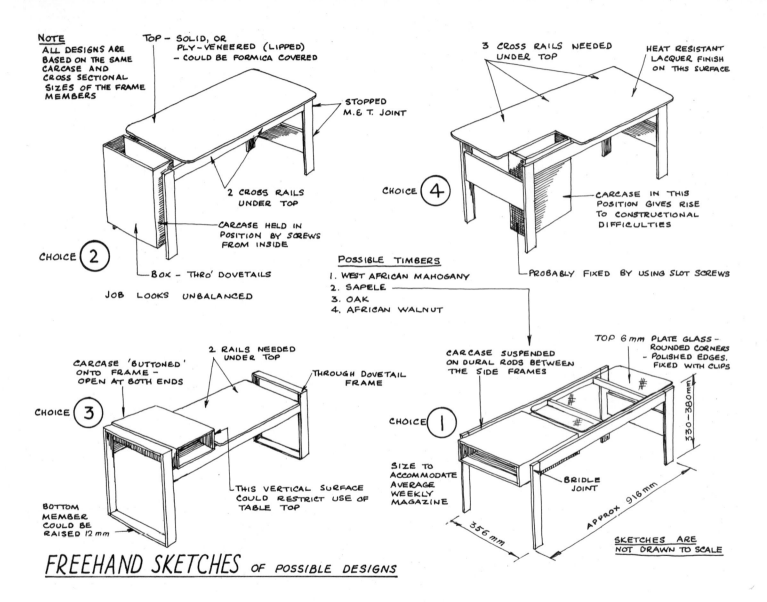

NOTE
ALL DESIGNS ARE BASED ON THE SAME CARCASE AND CROSS SECTIONAL SIZES OF THE FRAME MEMBERS

TOP - SOLID, OR PLY-VENEERED (LIPPED) - COULD BE FORMICA COVERED

STOPPED M.&T. JOINT

2 CROSS RAILS UNDER TOP

CARCASE HELD IN POSITION BY SCREWS FROM INSIDE

CHOICE ②

BOX - THRO' DOVETAILS

JOB LOOKS UNBALANCED

3 CROSS RAILS NEEDED UNDER TOP

HEAT RESISTANT LACQUER FINISH ON THIS SURFACE

CHOICE ④

CARCASE IN THIS POSITION GIVES RISE TO CONSTRUCTIONAL DIFFICULTIES

PROBABLY FIXED BY USING SLOT SCREWS

POSSIBLE TIMBERS
1. WEST AFRICAN MAHOGANY
2. SAPELE
3. OAK
4. AFRICAN WALNUT

CARCASE 'BUTTONED' ONTO FRAME - OPEN AT BOTH ENDS

2 RAILS NEEDED UNDER TOP

THROUGH DOVETAIL FRAME

CHOICE ③

BOTTOM MEMBER COULD BE RAISED 12 mm

THIS VERTICAL SURFACE COULD RESTRICT USE OF TABLE TOP

CARCASE SUSPENDED ON DURAL RODS BETWEEN THE SIDE FRAMES

TOP 6 mm PLATE GLASS - ROUNDED CORNERS - POLISHED EDGES. FIXED WITH CLIPS

CHOICE ①

SIZE TO ACCOMMODATE AVERAGE WEEKLY MAGAZINE

BRIDLE JOINT

330-380 mm

356 mm

APPROX 916 mm

SKETCHES ARE NOT DRAWN TO SCALE

FREEHAND SKETCHES OF POSSIBLE DESIGNS

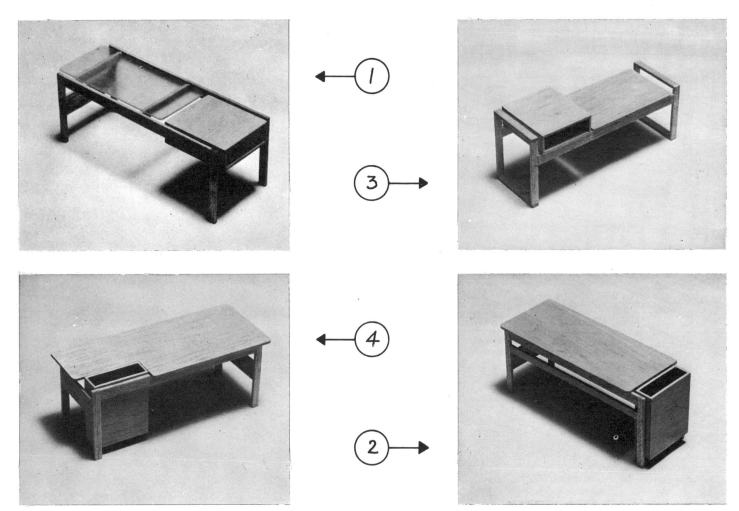

PHOTOGRAPHS BY TONY LEIGH

1/5 TH SCALE BALSA WOOD MODELS

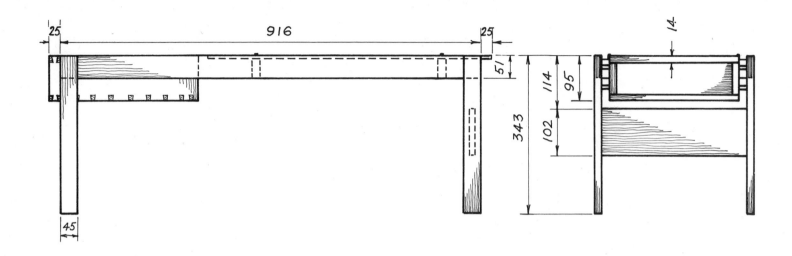

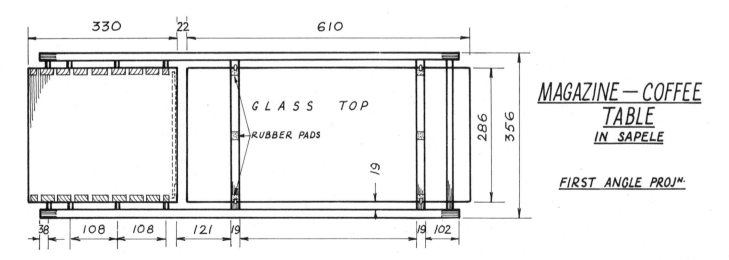

GLASS TOP

RUBBER PADS

MAGAZINE—COFFEE
TABLE
IN SAPELE

FIRST ANGLE PROJ^{N.}

EXAMPLE OF A WORKING DRAWING

ALL DIMENSIONS IN MMs

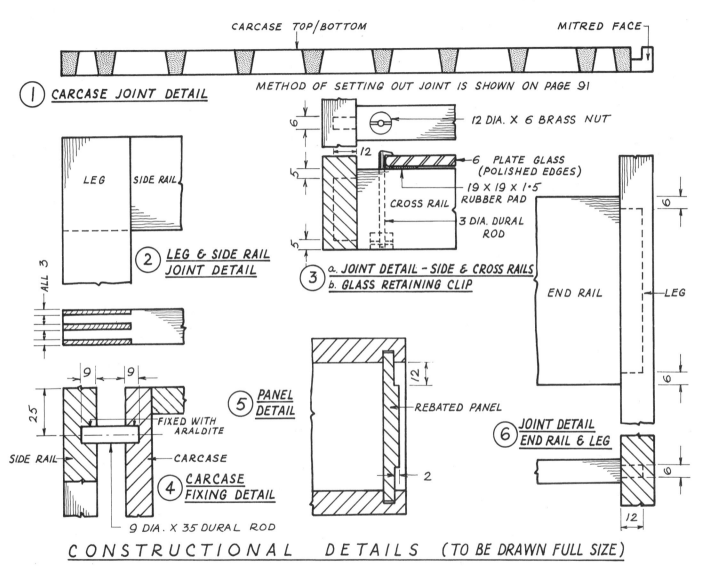

CARCASE TOP/BOTTOM

MITRED FACE

① CARCASE JOINT DETAIL   METHOD OF SETTING OUT JOINT IS SHOWN ON PAGE 91

LEG   SIDE RAIL

ALL 3

② LEG & SIDE RAIL JOINT DETAIL

6

12

12 DIA. X 6 BRASS NUT

5

6 PLATE GLASS (POLISHED EDGES)

CROSS RAIL

19 X 19 X 1·5 RUBBER PAD

5

3 DIA. DURAL ROD

③ a. JOINT DETAIL - SIDE & CROSS RAILS
b. GLASS RETAINING CLIP

END RAIL

LEG

6

6

9   9

25

FIXED WITH ARALDITE

SIDE RAIL   CARCASE

④ CARCASE FIXING DETAIL

9 DIA. X 35 DURAL ROD

⑤ PANEL DETAIL

12

REBATED PANEL

2

⑥ JOINT DETAIL END RAIL & LEG

6

12

CONSTRUCTIONAL DETAILS (TO BE DRAWN FULL SIZE)

ALL DIMENSIONS IN MMs

COFFEE TABLE
CUTTING & MATERIAL LIST

MM

NO. OFF	NAME OF PART	MATERIAL	L	W	T
2	SIDE RAILS	SAPELE	926	57	21
4	LEGS	—— do ——	356	44	21
2	UPPER RAILS FOR GLASS	—— do ——	356	50	21
1	LOWER CROSS RAIL	—— do ——	356	108	14
2	CARCASE SIDES	—— do ——	108	336	16
2	CARCASE TOP & BOTTOM	—— do ——	298	336	16
1	CARCASE BACK PANEL	—— do ——	279	86	11
4	GLASS RETAINING CLIPS	DURAL ROD	63		3 DIA.
4	NUTS	BRASS ROD	6		12 DIA.
6	RUBBER PADS	RUBBER SHEET	19	19	1·5
1	PLATE GLASS TOP	POLISHED EDGES	610	286	6
8	DISTANCE PIECES	DURAL ROD	35		9 DIA.

ALLOWANCES ON TIMBER SIZES — L + 12 : W + 6 : T + 1·5

OUTLINE PROCEDURE FOR MAKING THE TABLE

1. MAKE SIDE 'U' FRAMES
2. DRILL HOLES FOR DISTANCE PIECES
3. JOIN SIDE FRAMES TOGETHER BUT DO NOT GLUE
4. DRILL HOLES IN THE UPPER CROSS RAILS FOR GLASS RETAINING CLIPS
5. MAKE THE CARCASE
6. DRILL HOLES IN THE CARCASE SIDES FOR DISTANCE PIECES
7. MAKE DISTANCE PIECES AND ASSEMBLE ALL PARTS
8. MAKE RETAINING CLIPS AND RUBBER PADS. SECURE GLASS IN POSITION

PHOTOGRAPH BY TONY LEIGH   DESIGNED & MADE BY KEITH BOSWELL

THE   COMPLETED   PROJECT

DESIGN BRIEF
SALT & PEPPER POTS

INFORMATION

0.1 THEY ARE TO BE DESIGNED FROM A BASIC SECTION OF TIMBER 30MM X 30MM.

0.2 EASE OF FILLING AND HANDLING ARE ESSENTIAL.

0.3 MATERIAL AND FINISH MUST BE SUITABLE FOR THE INTENDED PURPOSE.

0.4 DISTINGUISHING FEATURES SHOULD BE APPARENT BUT THERE MUST ALSO BE A UNITY BETWEEN THE ITEMS.

0.5 THE PIECES ARE TO BE FREE STANDING.

PROGRAMME

1.1 LEAD UP SKETCHES.

1.2 PERSPECTIVE PRESENTATION SKETCHES USING COLOUR WASH.

1.3 FINAL SOLUTION SUITABLY CONSTRUCTED.

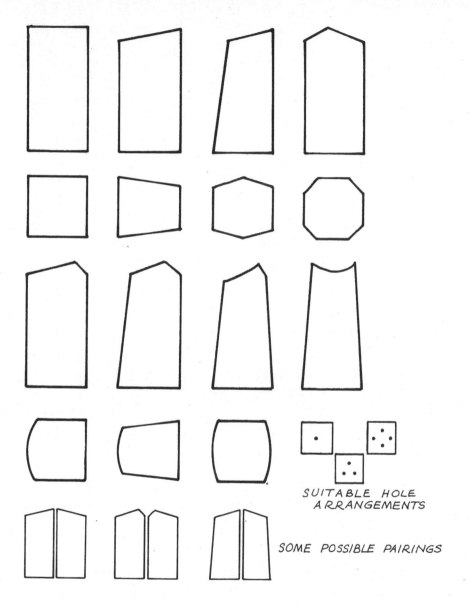

SUITABLE HOLE ARRANGEMENTS

SOME POSSIBLE PAIRINGS

CONSTRUCTION

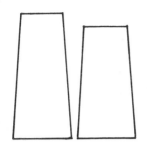

CHANGE OF HEIGHT COULD HELP TO DISTINGUISH SALT FROM PEPPER

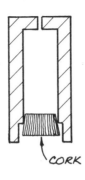

CORK

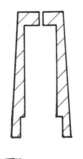

NOTE.
AFTER BORING BODY THICKNESS MUST ALLOW FOR ANY SHAPING

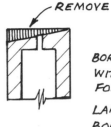

REMOVE

BORE HOLES WITH A MACHINE FORSTNER BIT

LARGE HOLE IS BORED FIRST FOLLOWED BY THE SMALLER ONE

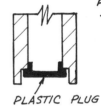

PLASTIC PLUG

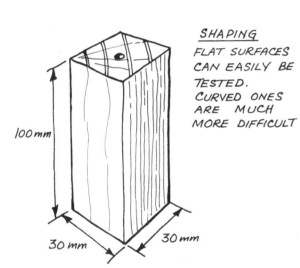

100 mm

30 mm   30 mm

ALWAYS SHAPE LAST

SHAPING
FLAT SURFACES CAN EASILY BE TESTED. CURVED ONES ARE MUCH MORE DIFFICULT

CONSIDER THE PROBLEM OF HOLDING WHEN SHAPING. THE SHAPE SHOULD COME NATURALLY FROM THE TOOLS USED

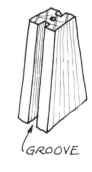

GROOVE

DESIGN BRIEF
PLYWOOD STRUCTURES

INFORMATION

0.1 DESIGN AN ITEM OR RELATED GROUP OF ITEMS OF FURNITURE CONSTRUCTED ENTIRELY FROM PLYWOOD.

0.2 YOUR AIM SHOULD BE TO EXPLOIT THE CHARACTERISTICS OF THIS SHEET MATERIAL IN MAKING 3 DIMENSIONAL STRUCTURES.

0.3 THE LAMINATING PROCESS TO PRODUCE A CURVED MEMBER SHOULD NOT BE USED.

PROGRAMME

1.1 LEAD UP SKETCHES AND ANALYTICAL NOTES.

1.2 PRESENTATION PERSPECTIVE SKETCHES USING COLOUR WASH.

1.3 1/5 TH SCALE MODEL IN RELATED MATERIALS AND COLOURS.

1.4 WORKING DRAWINGS.

1.5 FINAL SOLUTION SUITABLY CONSTRUCTED.

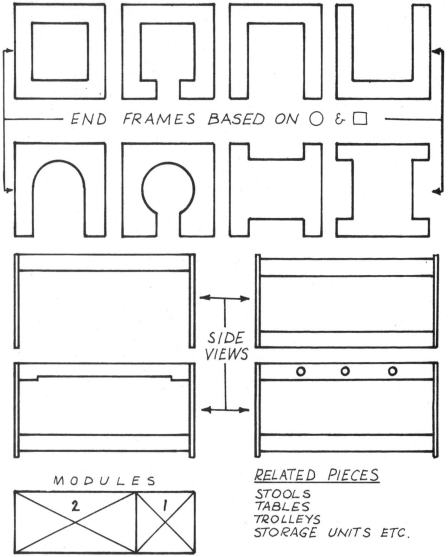

END FRAMES BASED ON ○ & □

SIDE VIEWS

MODULES

RELATED PIECES

STOOLS
TABLES
TROLLEYS
STORAGE UNITS ETC.

14

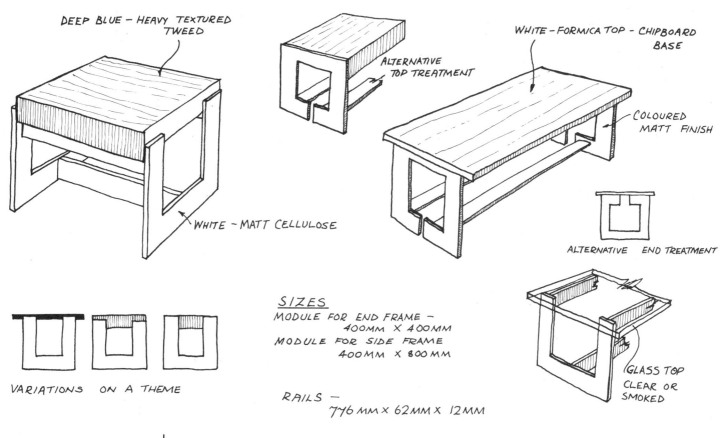

DEEP BLUE — HEAVY TEXTURED TWEED

ALTERNATIVE TOP TREATMENT

WHITE — FORMICA TOP — CHIPBOARD BASE

COLOURED MATT FINISH

WHITE — MATT CELLULOSE

ALTERNATIVE END TREATMENT

GLASS TOP CLEAR OR SMOKED

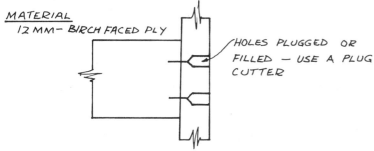

VARIATIONS ON A THEME

SIZES
MODULE FOR END FRAME —
400MM X 400MM
MODULE FOR SIDE FRAME
400MM X 800MM

RAILS —
776 MM X 62MM X 12MM

MATERIAL
12 MM — BIRCH FACED PLY

HOLES PLUGGED OR FILLED — USE A PLUG CUTTER

METHOD OF CONSTRUCTION — SCREW & GLUE

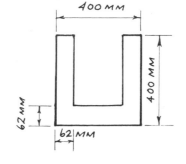

400 MM

400 MM

62 MM

62 MM

15

DESIGN BRIEF
LAMINATED CONSTRUCTIONS

INFORMATION

0.1 THE CONSTRUCTION MAY BE FUNCTIONAL OR DECORATIVE.

0.2 SHAPES MAY BE FORMED USING THE VACUUM PROCESS WITH A HEAVY DUTY PLASTIC BAG OR RUBBER ENVELOPE TOGETHER WITH A SUITABLE PUMP.

0.3 DEVELOP A MULTI PURPOSE FORMER FROM WHICH SEVERAL DESIGN SOLUTIONS CAN BE MADE.

0.4 THE LAMINATED FORMS MAY BE USED IN ISOLATION E.G. A TOAST RACK, OR USED IN CONJUNCTION WITH OTHER METHODS OF CONSTRUCTION E.G. PART OF A CHAIR OR SUPPORT FOR A TABLE TOP.

PROGRAMME

1.1 LEAD UP SKETCHES.

1.2 PERSPECTIVE PRESENTATION SKETCH USING COLOUR WASH.

1.3 MOCK UPS TO SUITABLE SCALE USING CARD ETC.

1.4 WORKING DRAWINGS.

1.5 FINAL SOLUTION SUITABLY CONSTRUCTED.

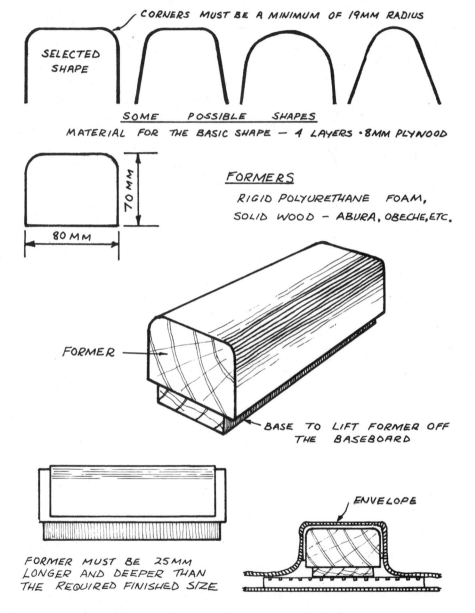

CORNERS MUST BE A MINIMUM OF 19MM RADIUS

SELECTED SHAPE

SOME POSSIBLE SHAPES

MATERIAL FOR THE BASIC SHAPE — 4 LAYERS ·8MM PLYWOOD

70 MM

80 MM

FORMERS

RIGID POLYURETHANE FOAM,

SOLID WOOD — ABURA, OBECHE, ETC.

FORMER

BASE TO LIFT FORMER OFF THE BASEBOARD

FORMER MUST BE 25MM LONGER AND DEEPER THAN THE REQUIRED FINISHED SIZE

ENVELOPE

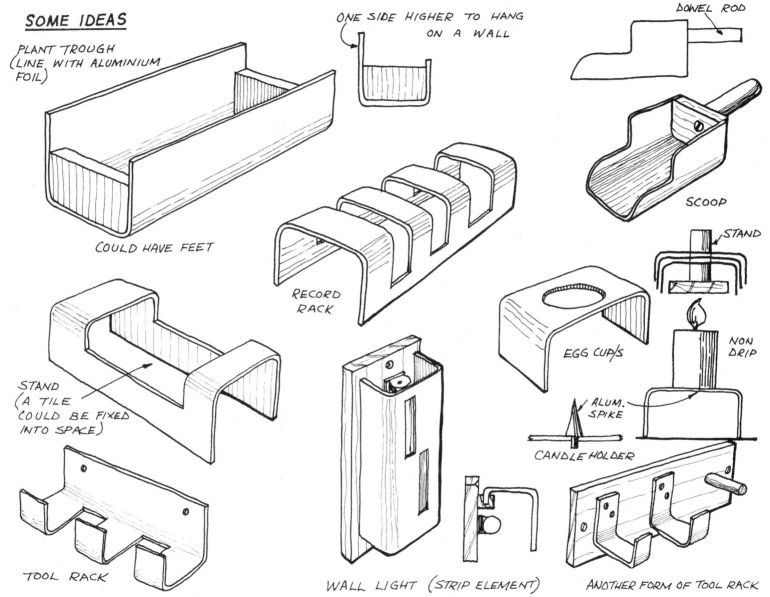

SOME IDEAS

PLANT TROUGH
(LINE WITH ALUMINIUM
FOIL)

ONE SIDE HIGHER TO HANG
ON A WALL

DOWEL ROD

COULD HAVE FEET

RECORD
RACK

SCOOP

STAND
(A TILE
COULD BE FIXED
INTO SPACE)

EGG CUP/S

STAND

NON
DRIP

ALUM.
SPIKE

CANDLE HOLDER

TOOL RACK

WALL LIGHT (STRIP ELEMENT)

ANOTHER FORM OF TOOL RACK

17

DESIGN BRIEF

JEWELLERY

INFORMATION

0.1 DESIGN AT LEAST THREE PIECES OF JEWELLERY USING WOOD AS THE BASIC MATERIAL BUT OTHER MEDIA MAY BE INTRODUCED AS REQUIRED.

0.2 THE RANGE OF WORK SHOULD BE SIMPLE IN FORM BUT SHOW A RELATED PROGRESSIVE STYLE OF DECORATION. THE LATTER SHOULD ARISE NATURALLY FROM THE TOOLS AND MATERIALS AVAILABLE E.G. DRILLED HOLES – PLASTIC – NON FERROUS SHEET ETC.

0.3 THE SANDWICH TYPE OF WORK INVOLVING LAYERS OF MATERIALS AND JUST SHAPED IS NOT VERY EFFECTIVE AND OTHER INTERESTING WAYS OF TREATMENT SHOULD BE LOOKED FOR.

0.4 THE SIZE OF WORK IS IMPORTANT IN RELATION TO THE HUMAN FORM AND VARYING TYPES OF CLOTHES WORN.

0.5 CLIPS MUST BE OBTAINED BEFORE DESIGNS ARE FINALISED.

PROGRAMME

1.1 LEAD UP SKETCHES.

1.2 PERSPECTIVE PRESENTATION SKETCHES USING COLOUR WASHES.

1.3 PURCHASE CLIPS ETC.

1.4 WORKING DRAWINGS.

1.5 FINAL SOLUTIONS SUITABLY CONSTRUCTED.

GEOMETRICAL FORMS AS A BASIS FOR FINAL SHAPES

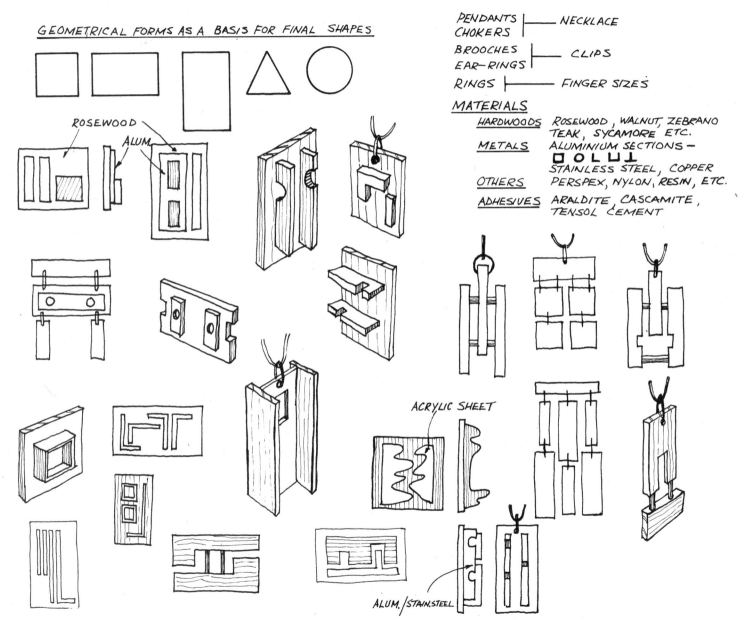

PENDANTS | ——— NECKLACE
CHOKERS |

BROOCHES |——— CLIPS
EAR-RINGS |

RINGS |——— FINGER SIZES

MATERIALS

HARDWOODS ROSEWOOD, WALNUT, ZEBRANO
TEAK, SYCAMORE ETC.

METALS ALUMINIUM SECTIONS —
▢ O L ⊔ ⊥
STAINLESS STEEL, COPPER

OTHERS PERSPEX, NYLON, RESIN, ETC.

ADHESIVES ARALDITE, CASCAMITE,
TENSOL CEMENT

ROSEWOOD

ALUM.

ACRYLIC SHEET

ALUM./STAIN.STEEL

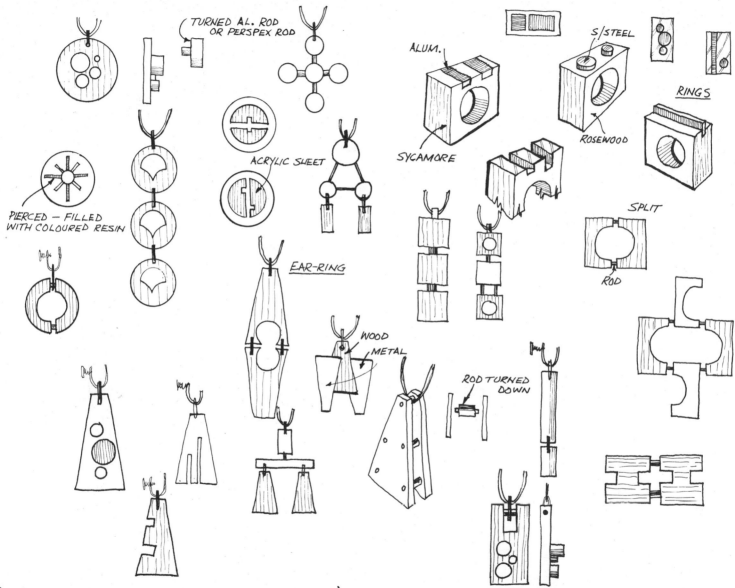

TURNED AL. ROD
OR PERSPEX ROD

ACRYLIC SHEET

PIERCED — FILLED
WITH COLOURED RESIN

EAR-RING

ALUM.

SYCAMORE

S/STEEL

ROSEWOOD

RINGS

SPLIT

ROD

WOOD

METAL

ROD TURNED
DOWN

20

JEWELLERY

AN ECONOMIC USE OF MATERIAL WHICH CAN BE FASHIONED INTO OBJECTS OF OUTSTANDING BEAUTY AND CHARM

PENDANTS BY M. CLARKSON

PENDANT BY P. SHORT

MATCHING PENDANT & EAR-RINGS
BY J. GRIFFITHS

RING BY J. GRIFFITHS

PENDANT BY M. HUGHES

BROOCH BY M. CLARKSON

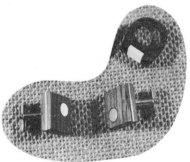

CUFF LINKS BY M. CLARKSON

EXAMPLES OF JEWELLERY MADE FROM SMALL PIECES OF FINE WOODS SUCH AS BLACK BEAN, BOXWOOD, ROSEWOOD, WALNUT & YEW, EMBELLISHED WITH SILVER, NICKEL SILVER, ALUMINIUM STAINLESS STEEL OR ACRYLIC

PREPARATION 1

MATERIAL
(TIMBER)

MAY BE OBTAINED IN ANY OF THESE FORMS

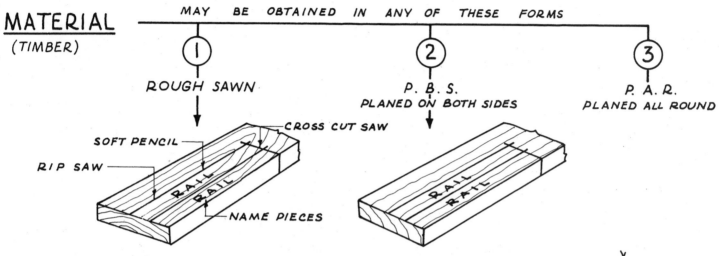

① ROUGH SAWN

② P. B. S.
PLANED ON BOTH SIDES

③ P. A. R.
PLANED ALL ROUND

SOFT PENCIL — CROSS CUT SAW

RIP SAW

RAIL RAIL

NAME PIECES

PIECES ARE NOW PREPARED TO CROSS SECTIONAL SIZE IN THE FOLLOWING ORDER :-

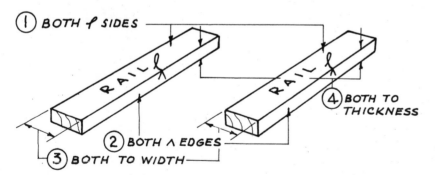

① BOTH ʄ SIDES

② BOTH ∧ EDGES

③ BOTH TO WIDTH

④ BOTH TO THICKNESS

NOTE REMOVE ANY UNEVENNESS FROM SURFACE WHICH IS TO BE PLACED ON THE BENCH — BEFORE PLANING ʄ SIDE

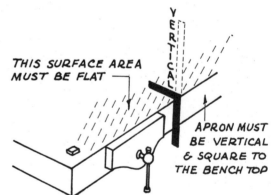

THIS SURFACE AREA MUST BE FLAT

VERTICAL

APRON MUST BE VERTICAL & SQUARE TO THE BENCH TOP

BEFORE PLANING CHECK YOUR BENCH TO SEE THAT THE TOP IS FLAT AND THE VICE & APRON ARE SQUARE TO IT

EARLY PLANNING IS ESSENTIAL TO OBTAIN THE BEST FINISHED RESULTS E.G.
WHERE POSSIBLE BOARDS SELECTED FOR CARCASE WORK SHOULD BE MARKED OUT AS UNDER :-

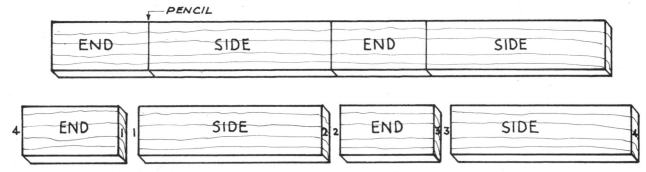

PENCIL

END · SIDE · END · SIDE

END · SIDE · END · SIDE

TO ENSURE CORRECT POSITIONING WHEN CUT UP PIECES ARE MARKED ON BOTH ENDS

PLANING THIN & WIDE BOARDS

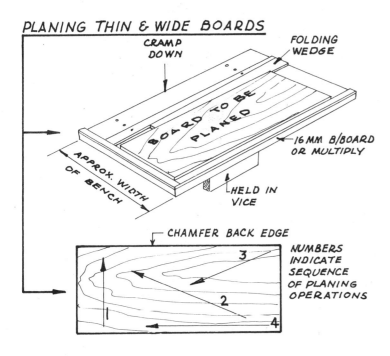

CRAMP DOWN

FOLDING WEDGE

BOARD TO BE PLANED

APPROX. WIDTH OF BENCH

16MM B/BOARD OR MULTIPLY

HELD IN VICE

CHAMFER BACK EDGE

NUMBERS INDICATE SEQUENCE OF PLANING OPERATIONS

3
2
1
4

PLANING END GRAIN

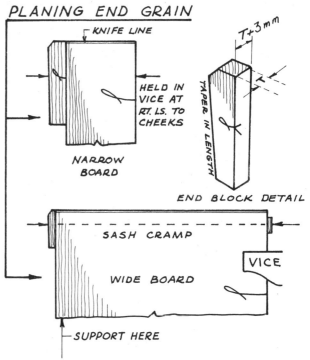

KNIFE LINE

HELD IN VICE AT RT. LS. TO CHEEKS

NARROW BOARD

$T+3mm$

T

TAPER IN LENGTH

END BLOCK DETAIL

SASH CRAMP

WIDE BOARD

VICE

SUPPORT HERE

PREPARATION 2

DIFFICULT GRAIN
(INTERLOCKED)

THIS MAY BE OVERCOME BY USING ONE OF THE METHODS SHOWN BELOW :-

① CLOSE UP THE MOUTH OF AN IRON PLANE

② SMOOTH SURFACE WITH CAB. SCRAPER

③ BACK-OFF CUTTING IRON OF SMOOTHER
(USED IN EXCEPTIONAL CASES)

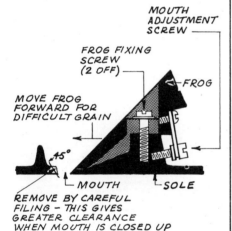

MOUTH ADJUSTMENT SCREW

FROG FIXING SCREW (2 OFF)

FROG

MOVE FROG FORWARD FOR DIFFICULT GRAIN

45°

MOUTH — SOLE

REMOVE BY CAREFUL FILING – THIS GIVES GREATER CLEARANCE WHEN MOUTH IS CLOSED UP

SECTIONAL VIEW OF METAL PLANE WITH ADJUSTABLE FROG

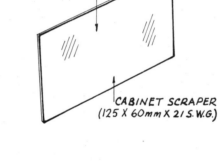

SAW BLADE STEEL

CABINET SCRAPER (125 X 60mm X 21 S.W.G.)

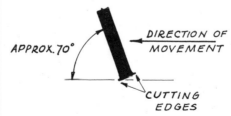

APPROX. 70°

DIRECTION OF MOVEMENT

CUTTING EDGES

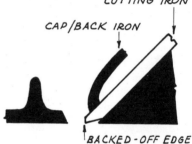

CUTTING IRON

CAP/BACK IRON

BACKED-OFF EDGE

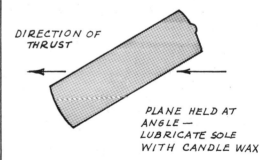

DIRECTION OF THRUST

PLANE HELD AT ANGLE — LUBRICATE SOLE WITH CANDLE WAX

FACTORS AFFECTING THE MAKING UP OF WIDE BOARDS

(1) SLASH SAWN BOARDS

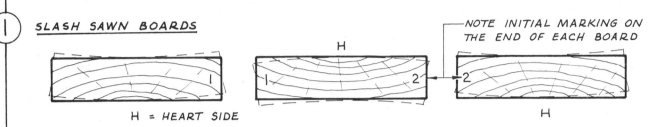

NOTE INITIAL MARKING ON THE END OF EACH BOARD

H = HEART SIDE

THE ARRANGEMENT SHOWN ABOVE HELPS TO MINIMISE THE EFFECT OF MOVEMENT OF THE BOARDS

(2) QUARTER SAWN BOARDS

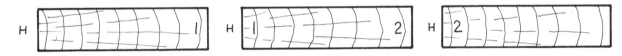

THE MOST STABLE FORM WHERE MOVEMENT IS LEAST PLUS GOOD FACE FIGURE

(3) WHERE GRAIN & FIGURE ARE OF PRIME IMPORTANCE

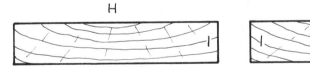

THIS ARRANGEMENT MAY HAVE TO BE RESORTED TO — AND SUBSEQUENT MOVEMENT ALLOWED FOR IN CONSTRUCTION

PROCEDURE WHEN JOINING BOARDS
1. PLANE 1 SIDE
2. PLANE 2 EDGE
3. MAKE JOINT BETWEEN 2 EDGES
4. GLUE IMMEDIATELY

'WIDENING' JOINTS
1. PLAIN BUTT
2. DOWELLED
3. 'LOOSE' TONGUE (PLY OR CROSS GRAINED)
4. TONGUE & GROOVE
5. SLOT SCREWED

SETTING OUT – 1

THE FRAME

ASSUME THE MATERIAL IS PREPARED TO X SECTIONAL SIZES

EXAMPLE — A STOPPED, HAUNCHED, MORTICE & TENON FRAME.

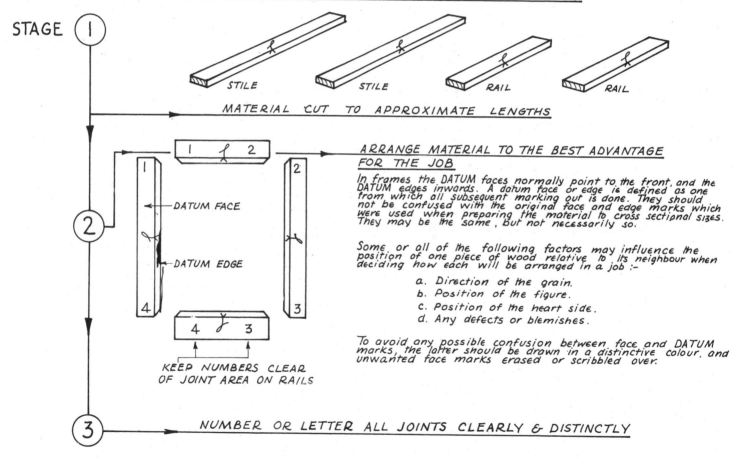

STAGE ①

STILE   STILE   RAIL   RAIL

MATERIAL CUT TO APPROXIMATE LENGTHS

②

DATUM FACE

DATUM EDGE

KEEP NUMBERS CLEAR
OF JOINT AREA ON RAILS

ARRANGE MATERIAL TO THE BEST ADVANTAGE
FOR THE JOB

In frames the DATUM faces normally point to the front, and the
DATUM edges inwards. A datum face or edge is defined as one
from which all subsequent marking out is done. They should
not be confused with the original face and edge marks which
were used when preparing the material to cross sectional sizes.
They may be the same, but not necessarily so.

Some or all of the following factors may influence the
position of one piece of wood relative to its neighbour when
deciding how each will be arranged in a job :-

    a. Direction of the grain.
    b. Position of the figure.
    c. Position of the heart side.
    d. Any defects or blemishes.

To avoid any possible confusion between face and DATUM
marks, the latter should be drawn in a distinctive colour, and
unwanted face marks erased or scribbled over.

③ NUMBER OR LETTER ALL JOINTS CLEARLY & DISTINCTLY

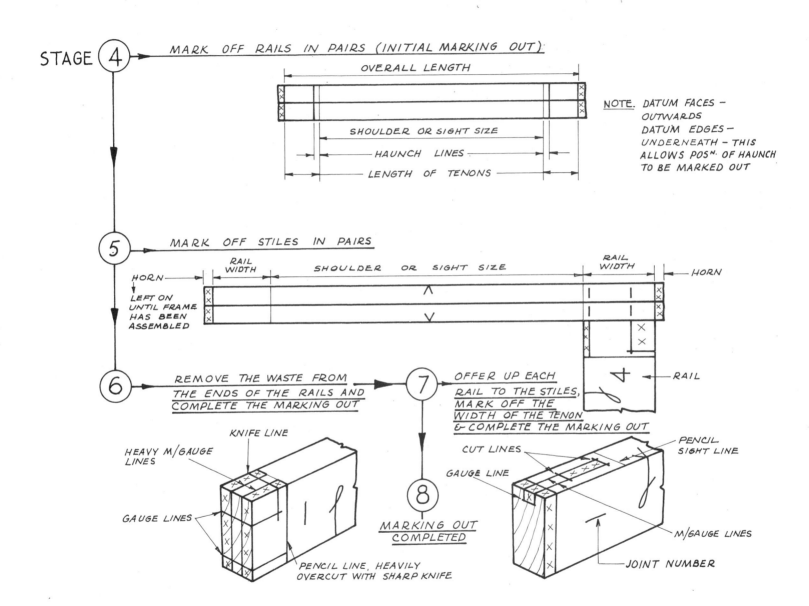

STAGE ④ → MARK OFF RAILS IN PAIRS (INITIAL MARKING OUT)

OVERALL LENGTH

SHOULDER OR SIGHT SIZE

HAUNCH LINES

LENGTH OF TENONS

NOTE. DATUM FACES –
OUTWARDS
DATUM EDGES –
UNDERNEATH – THIS
ALLOWS POSⁿ OF HAUNCH
TO BE MARKED OUT

⑤ → MARK OFF STILES IN PAIRS

RAIL WIDTH

SHOULDER OR SIGHT SIZE

RAIL WIDTH

HORN

HORN
LEFT ON
UNTIL FRAME
HAS BEEN
ASSEMBLED

RAIL

⑥ → REMOVE THE WASTE FROM THE ENDS OF THE RAILS AND COMPLETE THE MARKING OUT

⑦ → OFFER UP EACH RAIL TO THE STILES, MARK OFF THE WIDTH OF THE TENON & COMPLETE THE MARKING OUT

⑧ MARKING OUT COMPLETED

KNIFE LINE

HEAVY M/GAUGE LINES

GAUGE LINES

PENCIL LINE, HEAVILY OVERCUT WITH SHARP KNIFE

CUT LINES

PENCIL SIGHT LINE

GAUGE LINE

M/GAUGE LINES

JOINT NUMBER

27

SETTING OUT —2

THE CARCASE
ASSUME THE MATERIAL IS PREPARED TO X SECTIONAL SIZES

EXAMPLE —— A SIMPLE, THROUGH DOVETAILED BOX

STAGE ①

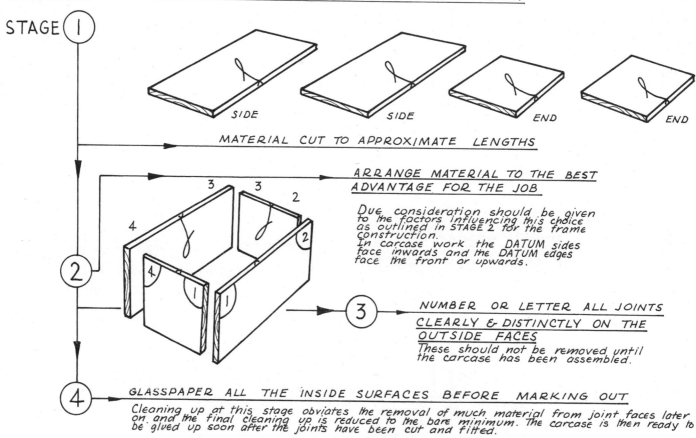

SIDE   SIDE   END   END

MATERIAL CUT TO APPROXIMATE LENGTHS

② ARRANGE MATERIAL TO THE BEST ADVANTAGE FOR THE JOB

Due consideration should be given to the factors influencing this choice as outlined in STAGE 2 for the frame construction.
In carcase work the DATUM sides face inwards and the DATUM edges face the front or upwards.

③ NUMBER OR LETTER ALL JOINTS CLEARLY & DISTINCTLY ON THE OUTSIDE FACES
These should not be removed until the carcase has been assembled.

④ GLASSPAPER ALL THE INSIDE SURFACES BEFORE MARKING OUT
Cleaning up at this stage obviates the removal of much material from joint faces later on and the final cleaning up is reduced to the bare minimum. The carcase is then ready to be glued up soon after the joints have been cut and fitted.

STAGE (5) MARK OFF SIDES AND ENDS IN PAIRS (INITIAL MARKING OUT)

METHOD A

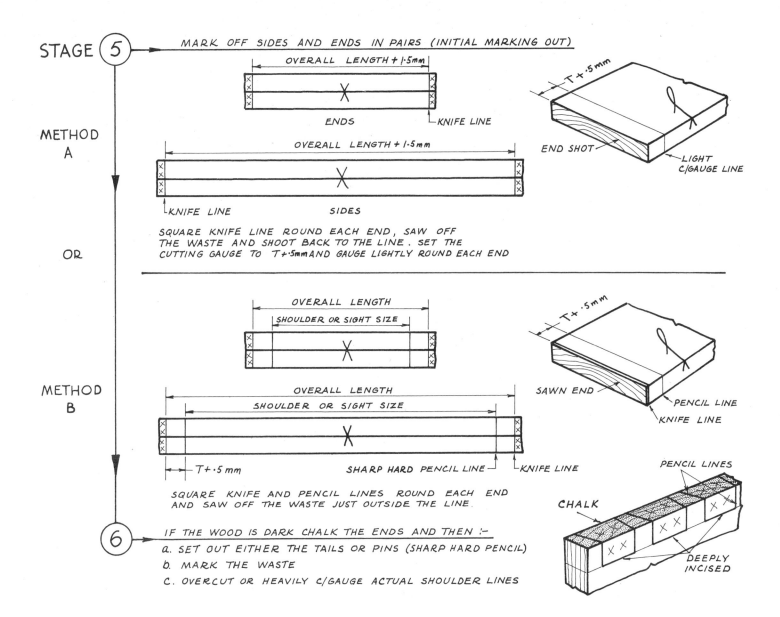

OVERALL LENGTH + 1·5mm

ENDS

KNIFE LINE

T + ·5mm

END SHOT

LIGHT C/GAUGE LINE

OVERALL LENGTH + 1·5mm

KNIFE LINE

SIDES

SQUARE KNIFE LINE ROUND EACH END, SAW OFF
THE WASTE AND SHOOT BACK TO THE LINE. SET THE
CUTTING GAUGE TO T+·5mm AND GAUGE LIGHTLY ROUND EACH END

OR

METHOD B

OVERALL LENGTH

SHOULDER OR SIGHT SIZE

T + ·5mm

SAWN END

PENCIL LINE

KNIFE LINE

OVERALL LENGTH

SHOULDER OR SIGHT SIZE

T + ·5 mm

SHARP HARD PENCIL LINE

KNIFE LINE

SQUARE KNIFE AND PENCIL LINES ROUND EACH END
AND SAW OFF THE WASTE JUST OUTSIDE THE LINE.

(6) IF THE WOOD IS DARK CHALK THE ENDS AND THEN :-

a. SET OUT EITHER THE TAILS OR PINS (SHARP HARD PENCIL)
b. MARK THE WASTE
c. OVERCUT OR HEAVILY C/GAUGE ACTUAL SHOULDER LINES

PENCIL LINES

CHALK

DEEPLY INCISED

SETTING OUT—3

THE STOOL OR SIMPLE TABLE   ASSUME THE MATERIAL IS PREPARED TO X SECTIONAL SIZES

EXAMPLE —— A STOOL WITH FOUR RAILS & STOPPED, HAUNCHED, M. & T. JOINTS

STAGE ①

LEGS – 4 OFF   SIDE RAILS – 2 OFF   END RAILS – 2 OFF

MATERIAL CUT TO APPROXIMATE LENGTHS

② ARRANGE MATERIAL TO THE BEST ADVANTAGE FOR THE JOB

─ MARKING THE TOP
OF THE LEGS AIDS
SUBSEQUENT LOCATION

LEGS – DATUM
FACE & EDGE
OUTWARDS

RAILS – DATUM
FACE OUTWARDS,
EDGE DOWNWARDS

NOTE.
DIRECTION OF THE
GRAIN IS IMPORTANT
AND MUST BE
TAKEN INTO
ACCOUNT WHEN
INITIAL SELECTION
IS MADE

③ NUMBER OR LETTER ALL JOINTS CLEARLY & DISTINCTLY AS SHOWN

STAGE (4) → MARK OFF RAILS IN PAIRS OR IF THEY ARE OF EQUAL LENGTH ALL TOGETHER

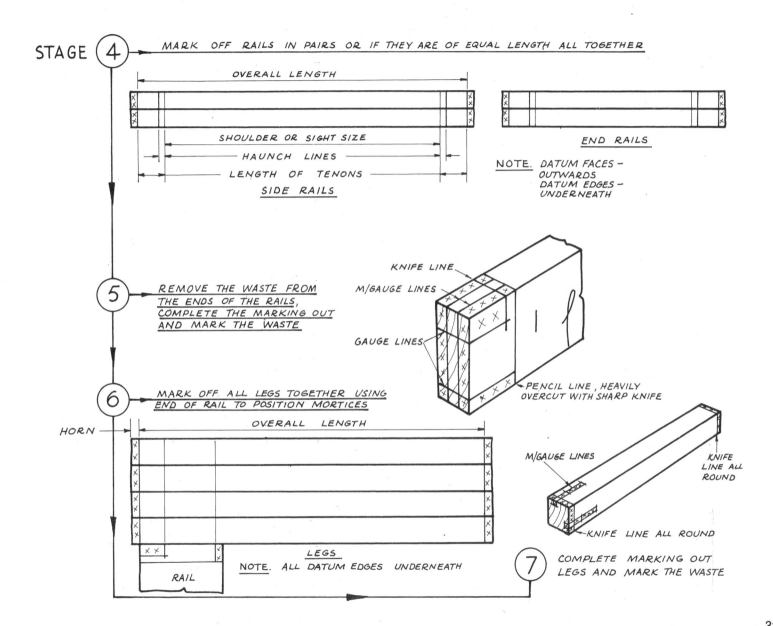

OVERALL LENGTH

SHOULDER OR SIGHT SIZE
HAUNCH LINES
LENGTH OF TENONS
SIDE RAILS

END RAILS

NOTE. DATUM FACES –
OUTWARDS
DATUM EDGES –
UNDERNEATH

(5) → REMOVE THE WASTE FROM
THE ENDS OF THE RAILS,
COMPLETE THE MARKING OUT
AND MARK THE WASTE

KNIFE LINE
M/GAUGE LINES

GAUGE LINES

PENCIL LINE, HEAVILY
OVERCUT WITH SHARP KNIFE

(6) → MARK OFF ALL LEGS TOGETHER USING
END OF RAIL TO POSITION MORTICES

HORN →

OVERALL LENGTH

RAIL

LEGS

NOTE. ALL DATUM EDGES UNDERNEATH

M/GAUGE LINES

KNIFE
LINE ALL
ROUND

KNIFE LINE ALL ROUND

(7) COMPLETE MARKING OUT
LEGS AND MARK THE WASTE

31

REMOVAL OF WASTE

STAGE	PROCEDURE	TOOLS USED
1	CLEARLY DEFINE BOUNDARY LINE	KNIFE : GAUGE (MARKING, CUTTING, MORTICE) : PENCIL IN SPECIAL CASES
2	MARK WASTE TO BE REMOVED	PENCIL (SOFT OR COLOURED)
3	REMOVE MAJORITY OF WASTE AS EASILY & AS QUICKLY AS POSSIBLE	SAW (TENON, COPING) : PLANE : BORING BIT : CHISEL IN SPECIAL CASES
4	CAREFULLY REMOVE SMALL AMOUNT OF WASTE LEFT, BACK TO BOUNDARY LINE	PLANE : CHISEL

NOTE.
AT EACH STAGE
WORK MUST
BE HELD FIRMLY
BY A CRAMPING DEVICE

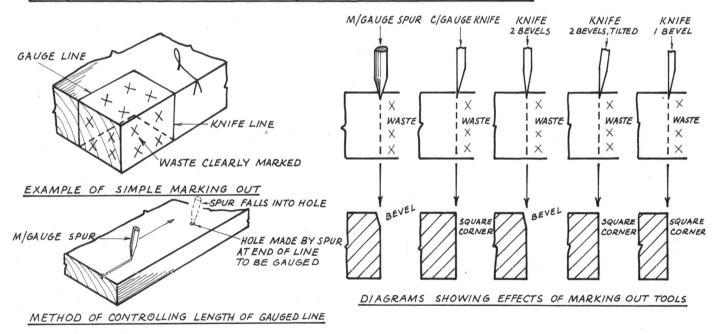

GAUGE LINE

KNIFE LINE

WASTE CLEARLY MARKED

EXAMPLE OF SIMPLE MARKING OUT

SPUR FALLS INTO HOLE

M/GAUGE SPUR

HOLE MADE BY SPUR AT END OF LINE TO BE GAUGED

METHOD OF CONTROLLING LENGTH OF GAUGED LINE

M/GAUGE SPUR   C/GAUGE KNIFE   KNIFE 2 BEVELS   KNIFE 2 BEVELS, TILTED   KNIFE 1 BEVEL

WASTE   WASTE   WASTE   WASTE   WASTE

BEVEL   SQUARE CORNER   BEVEL   SQUARE CORNER   SQUARE CORNER

DIAGRAMS SHOWING EFFECTS OF MARKING OUT TOOLS

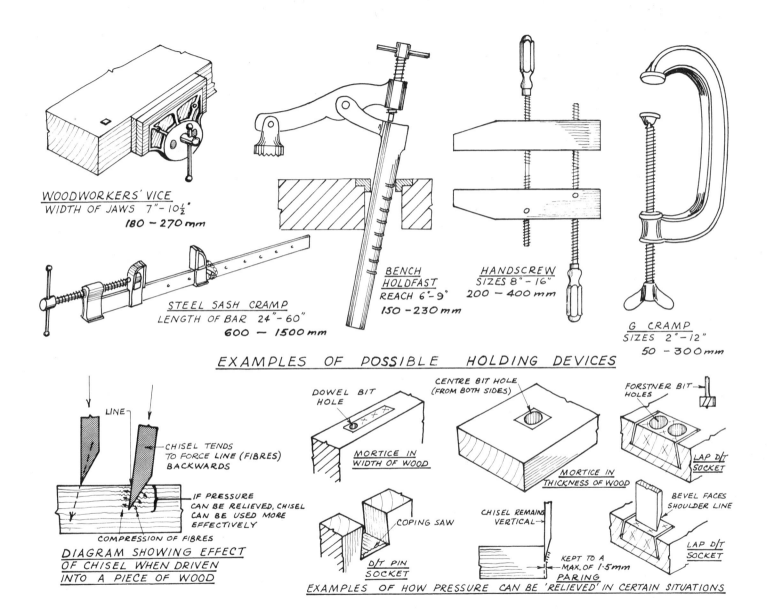

WOODWORKERS' VICE
WIDTH OF JAWS 7"-10½"
180 - 270 mm

STEEL SASH CRAMP
LENGTH OF BAR 24"- 60"
600 — 1500 mm

BENCH
HOLDFAST
REACH 6"-9"
150 - 230 mm

HANDSCREW
SIZES 8"- 16"
200 - 400 mm

G CRAMP
SIZES 2"- 12"
50 - 300mm

EXAMPLES OF POSSIBLE HOLDING DEVICES

LINE

CHISEL TENDS
TO FORCE LINE (FIBRES)
BACKWARDS

IF PRESSURE
CAN BE RELIEVED, CHISEL
CAN BE USED MORE
EFFECTIVELY

COMPRESSION OF FIBRES

DIAGRAM SHOWING EFFECT
OF CHISEL WHEN DRIVEN
INTO A PIECE OF WOOD

DOWEL BIT
HOLE

MORTICE IN
WIDTH OF WOOD

CENTRE BIT HOLE
(FROM BOTH SIDES)

MORTICE IN
THICKNESS OF WOOD

FORSTNER BIT
HOLES

LAP D/T
SOCKET

BEVEL FACES
SHOULDER LINE

LAP D/T
SOCKET

COPING SAW

D/T PIN
SOCKET

CHISEL REMAINS
VERTICAL

KEPT TO A
MAX. OF 1·5mm

PARING

EXAMPLES OF HOW PRESSURE CAN BE 'RELIEVED' IN CERTAIN SITUATIONS

GROOVING —1

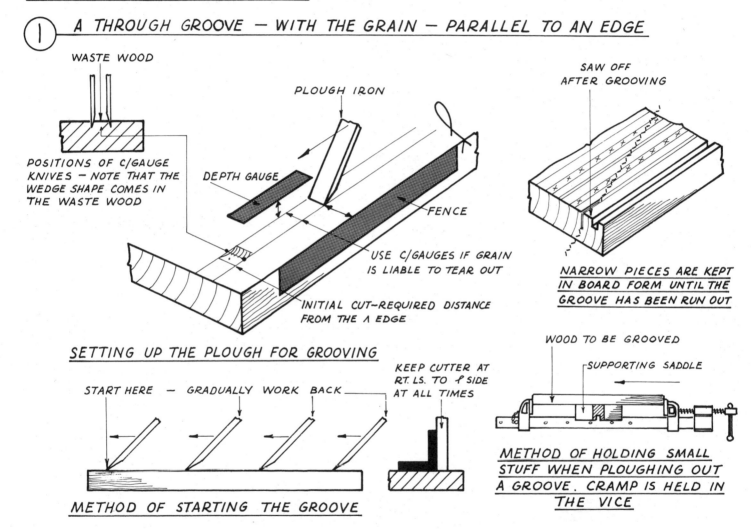

WASTE WOOD

PLOUGH IRON

SAW OFF AFTER GROOVING

POSITIONS OF C/GAUGE KNIVES — NOTE THAT THE WEDGE SHAPE COMES IN THE WASTE WOOD

DEPTH GAUGE

FENCE

USE C/GAUGES IF GRAIN IS LIABLE TO TEAR OUT

INITIAL CUT-REQUIRED DISTANCE FROM THE ∧ EDGE

NARROW PIECES ARE KEPT IN BOARD FORM UNTIL THE GROOVE HAS BEEN RUN OUT

SETTING UP THE PLOUGH FOR GROOVING

START HERE — GRADUALLY WORK BACK

KEEP CUTTER AT RT. LS. TO ∤ SIDE AT ALL TIMES

METHOD OF STARTING THE GROOVE

WOOD TO BE GROOVED

SUPPORTING SADDLE

METHOD OF HOLDING SMALL STUFF WHEN PLOUGHING OUT A GROOVE. CRAMP IS HELD IN THE VICE

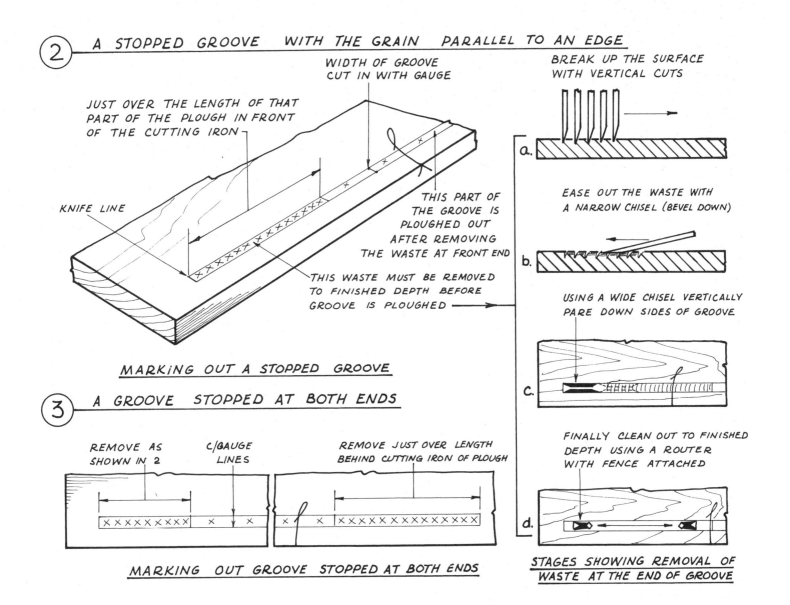

② A STOPPED GROOVE WITH THE GRAIN PARALLEL TO AN EDGE

WIDTH OF GROOVE CUT IN WITH GAUGE

JUST OVER THE LENGTH OF THAT PART OF THE PLOUGH IN FRONT OF THE CUTTING IRON

KNIFE LINE

THIS PART OF THE GROOVE IS PLOUGHED OUT AFTER REMOVING THE WASTE AT FRONT END

THIS WASTE MUST BE REMOVED TO FINISHED DEPTH BEFORE GROOVE IS PLOUGHED

MARKING OUT A STOPPED GROOVE

③ A GROOVE STOPPED AT BOTH ENDS

REMOVE AS SHOWN IN 2

C/GAUGE LINES

REMOVE JUST OVER LENGTH BEHIND CUTTING IRON OF PLOUGH

MARKING OUT GROOVE STOPPED AT BOTH ENDS

BREAK UP THE SURFACE WITH VERTICAL CUTS

a.

EASE OUT THE WASTE WITH A NARROW CHISEL (BEVEL DOWN)

b.

USING A WIDE CHISEL VERTICALLY PARE DOWN SIDES OF GROOVE

c.

FINALLY CLEAN OUT TO FINISHED DEPTH USING A ROUTER WITH FENCE ATTACHED

d.

STAGES SHOWING REMOVAL OF WASTE AT THE END OF GROOVE

GROOVING—2

A THROUGH GROOVE — ACROSS THE GRAIN—PARALLEL TO AN END

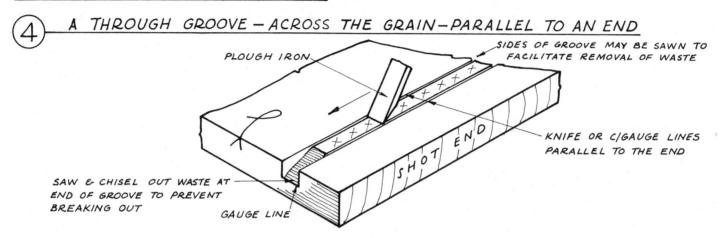

PLOUGH IRON

SIDES OF GROOVE MAY BE SAWN TO FACILITATE REMOVAL OF WASTE

KNIFE OR C/GAUGE LINES PARALLEL TO THE END

SHOT END

SAW & CHISEL OUT WASTE AT END OF GROOVE TO PREVENT BREAKING OUT

GAUGE LINE

PLOUGHING GROOVE AT RT. LS. TO GRAIN

⑤ A THROUGH GROOVE AT AN ANGLE TO THE GRAIN

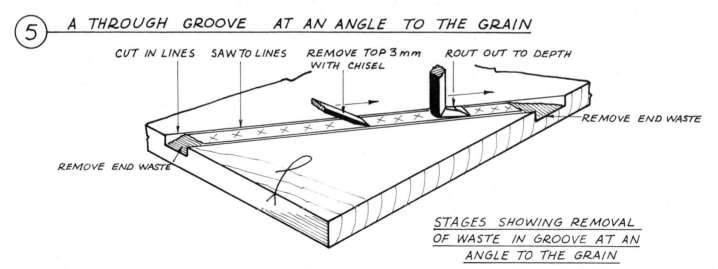

CUT IN LINES   SAW TO LINES   REMOVE TOP 3 mm WITH CHISEL   ROUT OUT TO DEPTH

REMOVE END WASTE

REMOVE END WASTE

STAGES SHOWING REMOVAL OF WASTE IN GROOVE AT AN ANGLE TO THE GRAIN

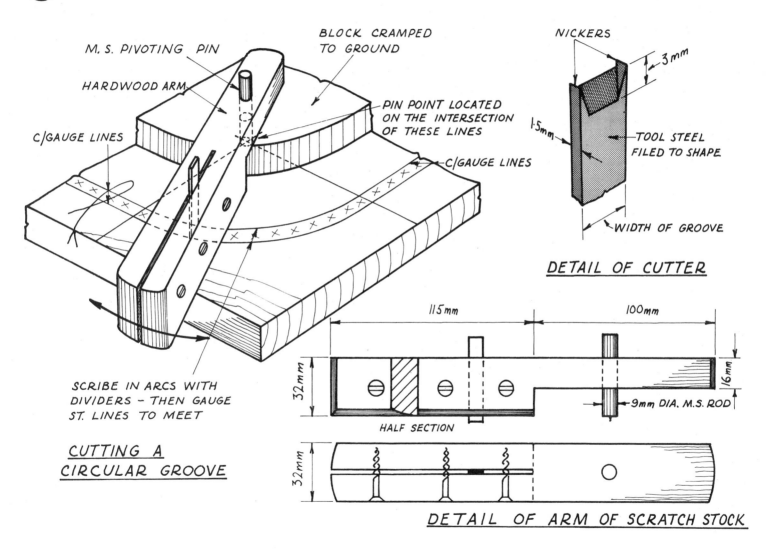

M.S. PIVOTING PIN

BLOCK CRAMPED TO GROUND

HARDWOOD ARM

PIN POINT LOCATED ON THE INTERSECTION OF THESE LINES

C/GAUGE LINES

C/GAUGE LINES

NICKERS

3mm

1.5mm

TOOL STEEL FILED TO SHAPE

WIDTH OF GROOVE

DETAIL OF CUTTER

SCRIBE IN ARCS WITH DIVIDERS — THEN GAUGE ST. LINES TO MEET

CUTTING A CIRCULAR GROOVE

115mm

100mm

32mm

16mm

HALF SECTION

9mm DIA. M.S. ROD

32mm

DETAIL OF ARM OF SCRATCH STOCK

REBATING —1

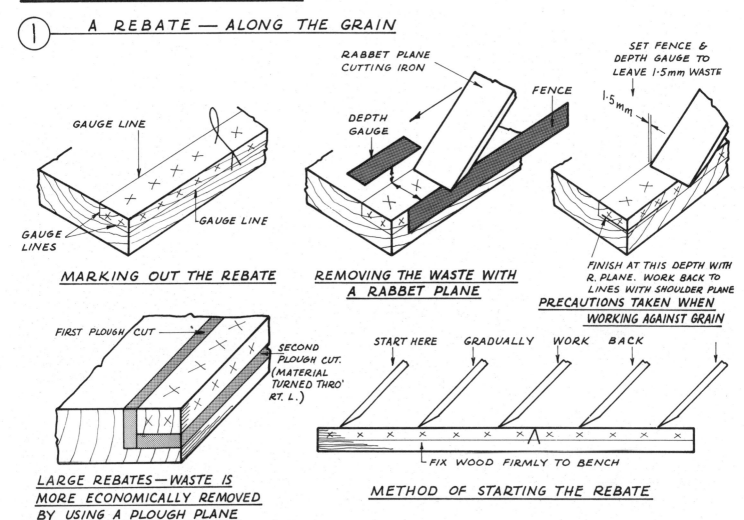

GAUGE LINE

GAUGE LINE

GAUGE LINES

MARKING OUT THE REBATE

RABBET PLANE
CUTTING IRON

DEPTH
GAUGE

FENCE

**REMOVING THE WASTE WITH
A RABBET PLANE**

SET FENCE &
DEPTH GAUGE TO
LEAVE 1·5mm WASTE

1·5mm

FINISH AT THIS DEPTH WITH
R. PLANE. WORK BACK TO
LINES WITH SHOULDER PLANE

**PRECAUTIONS TAKEN WHEN
WORKING AGAINST GRAIN**

FIRST PLOUGH CUT

SECOND
PLOUGH CUT.
(MATERIAL
TURNED THRO'
RT. L.)

**LARGE REBATES—WASTE IS
MORE ECONOMICALLY REMOVED
BY USING A PLOUGH PLANE**

START HERE   GRADUALLY   WORK   BACK

FIX WOOD FIRMLY TO BENCH

METHOD OF STARTING THE REBATE

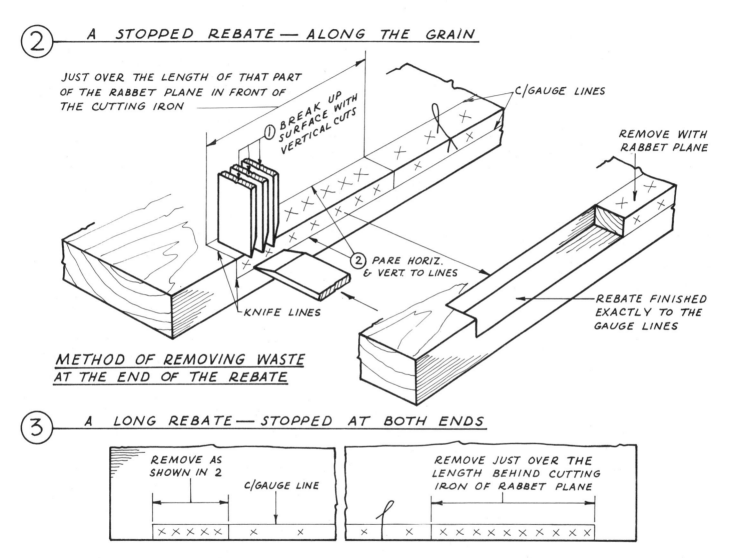

② A STOPPED REBATE — ALONG THE GRAIN

JUST OVER THE LENGTH OF THAT PART OF THE RABBET PLANE IN FRONT OF THE CUTTING IRON

① BREAK UP SURFACE WITH VERTICAL CUTS

C/GAUGE LINES

② PARE HORIZ. & VERT. TO LINES

KNIFE LINES

REMOVE WITH RABBET PLANE

REBATE FINISHED EXACTLY TO THE GAUGE LINES

METHOD OF REMOVING WASTE AT THE END OF THE REBATE

③ A LONG REBATE — STOPPED AT BOTH ENDS

REMOVE AS SHOWN IN 2

C/GAUGE LINE

REMOVE JUST OVER THE LENGTH BEHIND CUTTING IRON OF RABBET PLANE

MARKING OUT REBATE STOPPED AT BOTH ENDS

REBATING—2

④ **A REBATE—ACROSS THE GRAIN**

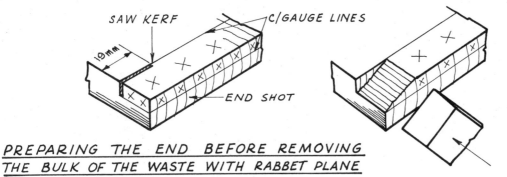

SAW KERF

C/GAUGE LINES

19mm

END SHOT

NOTE
SET RABBET PLANE
IRON SHORT OF WIDTH
& DEPTH BY 1·5mm AND
FINISH WITH SHOULDER PLANE

PREPARING THE END BEFORE REMOVING THE BULK OF THE WASTE WITH RABBET PLANE

⑤ **A REBATE—ALONG END GRAIN**

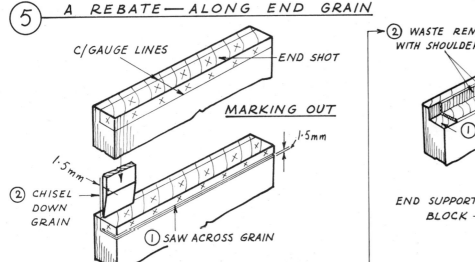

C/GAUGE LINES

END SHOT

MARKING OUT

1·5mm

1·5mm

② CHISEL DOWN GRAIN

① SAW ACROSS GRAIN

REMOVING BULK OF WASTE

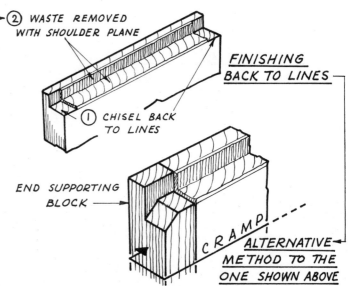

② WASTE REMOVED WITH SHOULDER PLANE

① CHISEL BACK TO LINES

FINISHING BACK TO LINES

END SUPPORTING BLOCK

CRAMP

ALTERNATIVE METHOD TO THE ONE SHOWN ABOVE

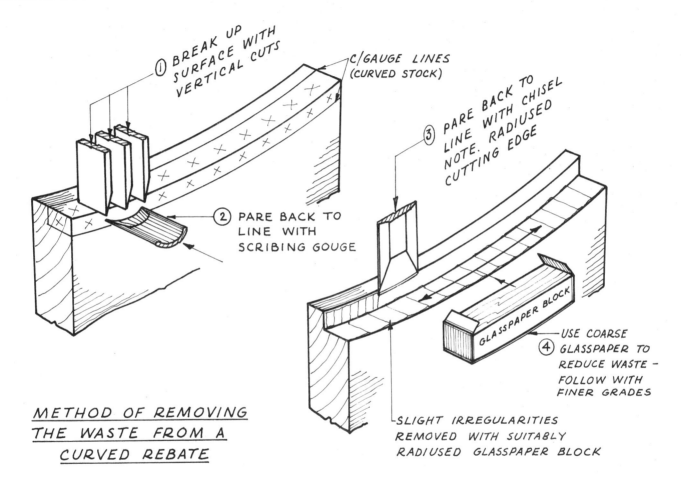

① BREAK UP SURFACE WITH VERTICAL CUTS

C/GAUGE LINES (CURVED STOCK)

③ PARE BACK TO LINE WITH CHISEL. NOTE. RADIUSED CUTTING EDGE

② PARE BACK TO LINE WITH SCRIBING GOUGE

GLASSPAPER BLOCK

④ USE COARSE GLASSPAPER TO REDUCE WASTE — FOLLOW WITH FINER GRADES

SLIGHT IRREGULARITIES REMOVED WITH SUITABLY RADIUSED GLASSPAPER BLOCK

METHOD OF REMOVING THE WASTE FROM A CURVED REBATE

BORING — 1

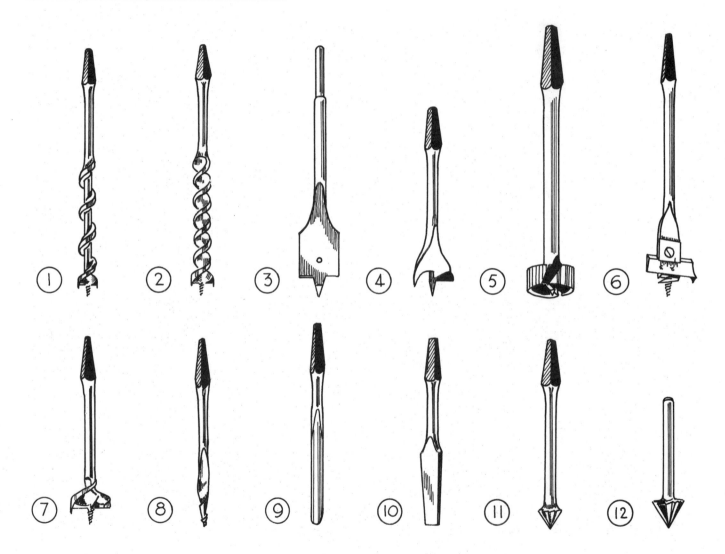

NO	NAME	SIZES IN MM	REMARKS
1	SOLID CENTRE AUGER BIT	3 — 38	GENERAL PURPOSE BIT
2	JENNINGS PAT. AUGER BIT	5 — 38	SUITABLE FOR HARDWOODS
3	RIDGWAY "FLATBIT"	9 — 32	USED IN ELECTRIC DRILLS
4	CENTRE BIT	6 — 57	USED FOR SHALLOW HOLES
5	FORSTNER PAT. BIT	9 — 50	PRODUCES FLAT BOTTOMED HOLES
6	EXPANSIVE BIT	No.1. 12-22 TO No.7. 114-152	PRIMARILY FOR SOFTWOODS
7	NEW PATTERN CENTRE BIT	5 — 57	USED FOR SHALLOW HOLES
8	COBRA BIT	1·5 — 9	LIABLE TO SPLIT THE WOOD
9	SHELL BIT	3 — 12	SUITABLE FOR END GRAIN
10	TURNSCREW BIT	6 — 16	EXTRA POWER FROM BRACE
11	ROSEHEAD COUNTERSINK	6 — 25	GIVES RECESS FOR CSK SCREW HD
12	ROSEHEAD COUNTERSINK	9 — 12	USED IN HAND DRILL

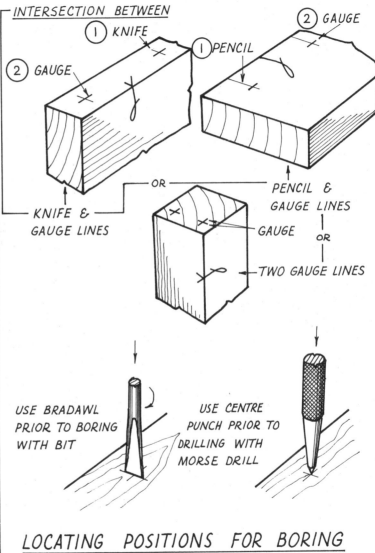

INTERSECTION BETWEEN
① KNIFE
② GAUGE
① PENCIL
② GAUGE

KNIFE & GAUGE LINES

OR

GAUGE

TWO GAUGE LINES

PENCIL & GAUGE LINES

OR

USE BRADAWL PRIOR TO BORING WITH BIT

USE CENTRE PUNCH PRIOR TO DRILLING WITH MORSE DRILL

LOCATING POSITIONS FOR BORING

BORING — 2

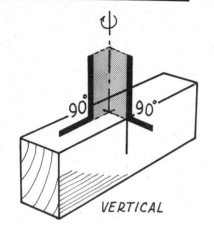

90° 90°

VERTICAL

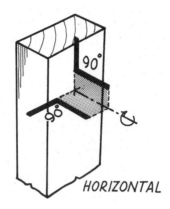

90°

HORIZONTAL

POSITIONS WHEN BORING

BORING AXIS MUST BE 'NORMAL' TO THE SURFACE

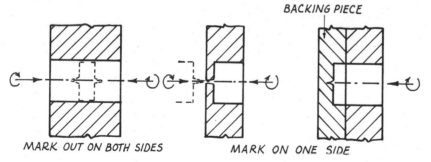

MARK OUT ON BOTH SIDES

MARK ON ONE SIDE

BACKING PIECE

EXAMPLES OF BORING TECHNIQUES

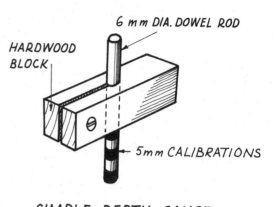

6 mm DIA. DOWEL ROD

HARDWOOD BLOCK

5mm CALIBRATIONS

SIMPLE DEPTH GAUGE

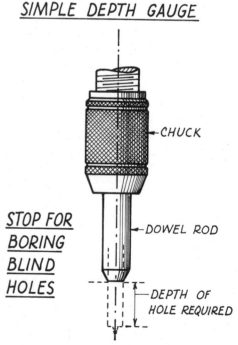

CHUCK

STOP FOR BORING BLIND HOLES

DOWEL ROD

DEPTH OF HOLE REQUIRED

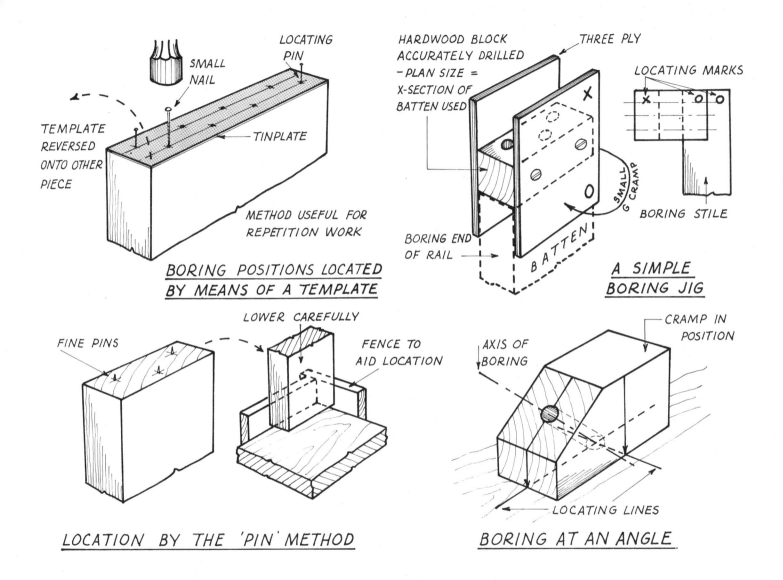

SMALL NAIL

LOCATING PIN

TEMPLATE REVERSED ONTO OTHER PIECE

TINPLATE

METHOD USEFUL FOR REPETITION WORK

BORING POSITIONS LOCATED BY MEANS OF A TEMPLATE

HARDWOOD BLOCK ACCURATELY DRILLED – PLAN SIZE = X-SECTION OF BATTEN USED

THREE PLY

LOCATING MARKS

BORING END OF RAIL

SMALL G CRAMP

BATTEN

BORING STILE

A SIMPLE BORING JIG

FINE PINS

LOWER CAREFULLY

FENCE TO AID LOCATION

LOCATION BY THE 'PIN' METHOD

CRAMP IN POSITION

AXIS OF BORING

LOCATING LINES

BORING AT AN ANGLE

CHAMFERS AND BEVELS

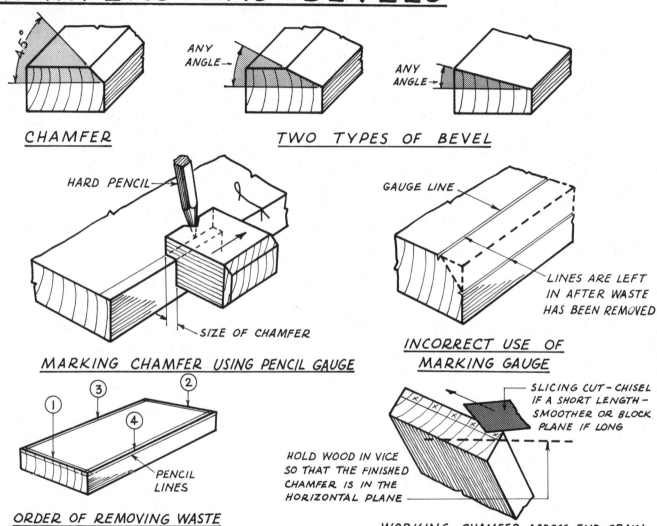

45°

CHAMFER

ANY ANGLE →

ANY ANGLE →

TWO TYPES OF BEVEL

HARD PENCIL →

SIZE OF CHAMFER

MARKING CHAMFER USING PENCIL GAUGE

GAUGE LINE

LINES ARE LEFT IN AFTER WASTE HAS BEEN REMOVED

INCORRECT USE OF MARKING GAUGE

① ③ ②
④

PENCIL LINES

ORDER OF REMOVING WASTE

SLICING CUT – CHISEL IF A SHORT LENGTH – SMOOTHER OR BLOCK PLANE IF LONG

HOLD WOOD IN VICE SO THAT THE FINISHED CHAMFER IS IN THE HORIZONTAL PLANE

WORKING CHAMFER ACROSS END GRAIN

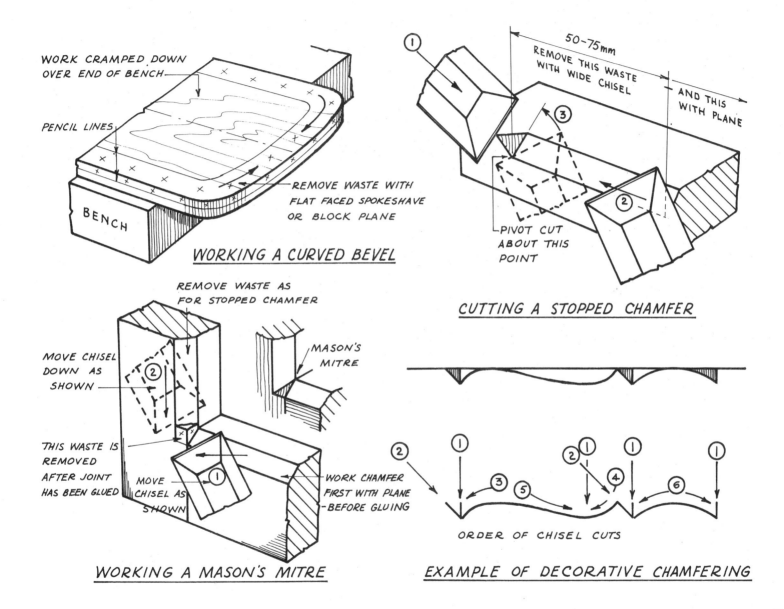

WORK CRAMPED DOWN OVER END OF BENCH

PENCIL LINES

BENCH

REMOVE WASTE WITH FLAT FACED SPOKESHAVE OR BLOCK PLANE

WORKING A CURVED BEVEL

① 50-75mm REMOVE THIS WASTE WITH WIDE CHISEL AND THIS WITH PLANE

③ ②

PIVOT CUT ABOUT THIS POINT

CUTTING A STOPPED CHAMFER

REMOVE WASTE AS FOR STOPPED CHAMFER

MOVE CHISEL DOWN AS SHOWN ②

MASON'S MITRE

THIS WASTE IS REMOVED AFTER JOINT HAS BEEN GLUED

MOVE CHISEL AS SHOWN ①

WORK CHAMFER FIRST WITH PLANE BEFORE GLUING

WORKING A MASON'S MITRE

② ① ② ① ① ①
③ ⑤ ④ ⑥

ORDER OF CHISEL CUTS

EXAMPLE OF DECORATIVE CHAMFERING

VENEERING—1

METHODS OF JOINTING

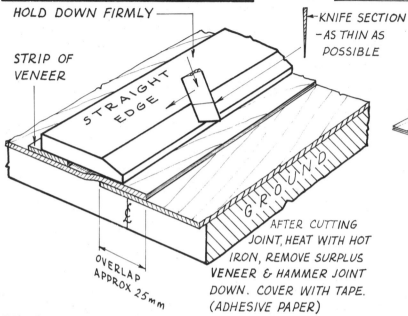

- HOLD DOWN FIRMLY
- KNIFE SECTION — AS THIN AS POSSIBLE
- STRIP OF VENEER
- STRAIGHT EDGE
- GROUND
- OVERLAP APPROX 25mm
- AFTER CUTTING JOINT, HEAT WITH HOT IRON, REMOVE SURPLUS VENEER & HAMMER JOINT DOWN. COVER WITH TAPE. (ADHESIVE PAPER)

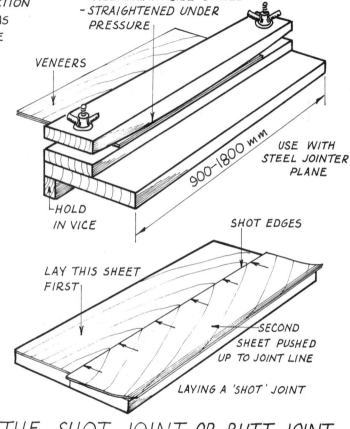

- UNDERNEATH SIDE CURVED — STRAIGHTENED UNDER PRESSURE
- VENEERS
- USE WITH STEEL JOINTER PLANE
- 900–1800 mm
- HOLD IN VICE
- SHOT EDGES
- LAY THIS SHEET FIRST
- SECOND SHEET PUSHED UP TO JOINT LINE
- LAYING A 'SHOT' JOINT

THE LAP JOINT

SUITABLE FOR MANY STRAIGHT GRAINED
AND EASILY WORKED VENEERS. e.g.
MAHOGANY , AFRICAN WALNUT ,
UTILE , STRAIGHT GRAINED WALNUT,
SYCAMORE , JAPANESE OAK ,
SAPELE , ELM.
SOME VENEERS TEND TO SPLIT IN FRONT
OF THE KNIFE AND THE JOINT HAS TO BE
MADE BY ANOTHER METHOD

THE SHOT JOINT OR BUTT JOINT

THE MODIFIED SHOOTING BOARD SHOWN ABOVE
HOLDS THE VENEERS FIRMLY WHEN PLANING THE
EDGES. ROSEWOOD, INDIAN LAUREL, & SOME OF
THE OAKS NEED JOINTING BY THIS METHOD

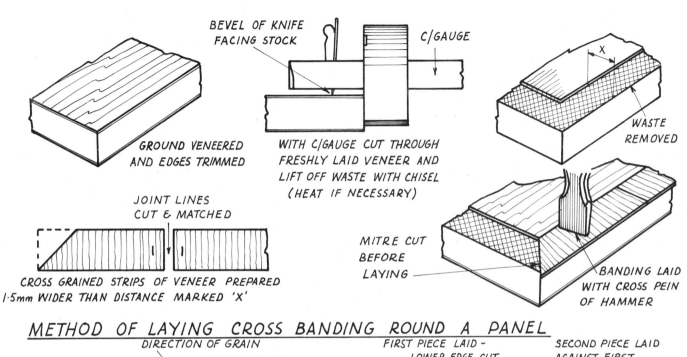

BEVEL OF KNIFE FACING STOCK

C/GAUGE

GROUND VENEERED AND EDGES TRIMMED

WITH C/GAUGE CUT THROUGH FRESHLY LAID VENEER AND LIFT OFF WASTE WITH CHISEL (HEAT IF NECESSARY)

X

WASTE REMOVED

JOINT LINES CUT & MATCHED

CROSS GRAINED STRIPS OF VENEER PREPARED 1·5mm WIDER THAN DISTANCE MARKED 'X'

MITRE CUT BEFORE LAYING

BANDING LAID WITH CROSS PEIN OF HAMMER

METHOD OF LAYING CROSS BANDING ROUND A PANEL

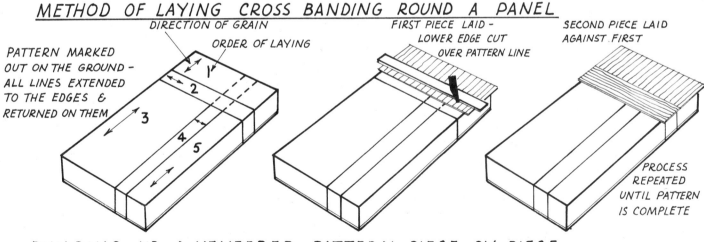

DIRECTION OF GRAIN

ORDER OF LAYING

PATTERN MARKED OUT ON THE GROUND - ALL LINES EXTENDED TO THE EDGES & RETURNED ON THEM

FIRST PIECE LAID - LOWER EDGE CUT OVER PATTERN LINE

SECOND PIECE LAID AGAINST FIRST

PROCESS REPEATED UNTIL PATTERN IS COMPLETE

BUILDING UP A VENEERED PATTERN PIECE BY PIECE

VENEERING-2

LAYING BY THE CAUL METHOD

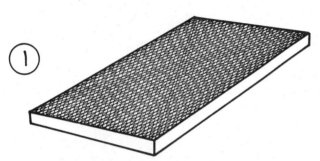

1

BASE FOR VENEER (GROUND)
TOOTHED ON BOTH SIDES

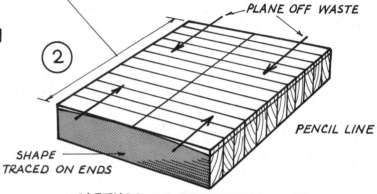

2

HOLD FIRMLY IN SASH CRAMPS WHEN PLANING

PLANE OFF WASTE

PENCIL LINE

SHAPE TRACED ON ENDS

METHOD OF PRODUCING UNIFORMLY SHAPED BEARERS

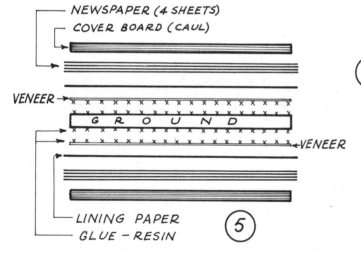

NEWSPAPER (4 SHEETS)

COVER BOARD (CAUL)

VENEER →

G R O U N D

← VENEER

LINING PAPER

GLUE – RESIN

5

EXPLODED DETAIL – READY FOR CRAMPING

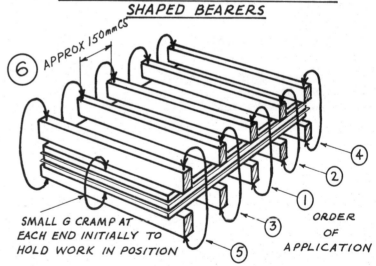

6

APPROX 150mmCS

SMALL G CRAMP AT EACH END INITIALLY TO HOLD WORK IN POSITION

ORDER OF APPLICATION

4

2

1

3

5

CRAMPING DETAIL

50

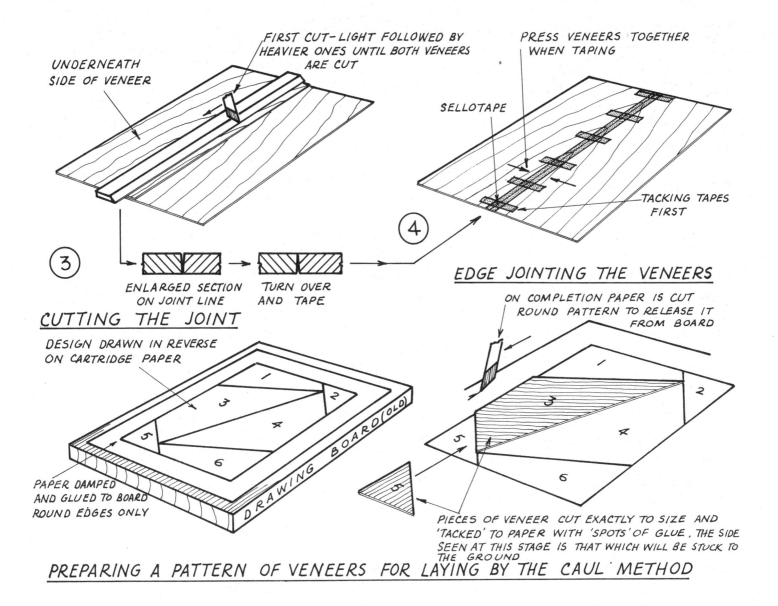

UNDERNEATH SIDE OF VENEER

FIRST CUT–LIGHT FOLLOWED BY HEAVIER ONES UNTIL BOTH VENEERS ARE CUT

PRESS VENEERS TOGETHER WHEN TAPING

SELLOTAPE

TACKING TAPES FIRST

③

ENLARGED SECTION ON JOINT LINE

TURN OVER AND TAPE

④

CUTTING THE JOINT

EDGE JOINTING THE VENEERS

DESIGN DRAWN IN REVERSE ON CARTRIDGE PAPER

ON COMPLETION PAPER IS CUT ROUND PATTERN TO RELEASE IT FROM BOARD

DRAWING BOARD (OLD)

PAPER DAMPED AND GLUED TO BOARD ROUND EDGES ONLY

PIECES OF VENEER CUT EXACTLY TO SIZE AND 'TACKED' TO PAPER WITH 'SPOTS' OF GLUE, THE SIDE SEEN AT THIS STAGE IS THAT WHICH WILL BE STUCK TO THE GROUND

PREPARING A PATTERN OF VENEERS FOR LAYING BY THE CAUL METHOD

VENEERING – 3   VACUUM ENVELOPE TECHNIQUE

PRINCIPLE INVOLVED – EVACUATION OF AIR FROM SEALED ENVELOPE WHICH CAN BE OF HEAVY RUBBER (INDUSTRIAL) OR FOR SMALLER WORK A THICK POLYTHENE BAG OR LARGE LORRY OR BUS INNER TUBES

METHOD – THE WORK IS PLACED BETWEEN TWO FLAT CAULS IN THE ENVELOPE. THE OPEN END IS SEALED AND THE AIR EVACUATED SO THAT ATMOSPHERIC PRESSURE (15 LBS P.S.I.) FORCES THE ENVELOPE INTO CONTACT WITH THE WORK PRESSING THE VENEERS AGAINST THE GROUND

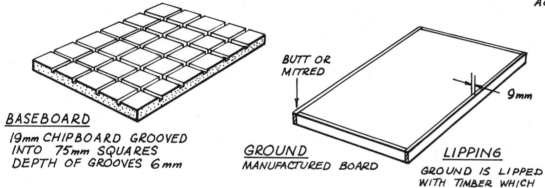

BASEBOARD
19mm CHIPBOARD GROOVED INTO 75mm SQUARES DEPTH OF GROOVES 6mm

BUTT OR MITRED

GROUND
MANUFACTURED BOARD

9mm

LIPPING
GROUND IS LIPPED WITH TIMBER WHICH MATCHES THE VENEER

2mm PROUD

AVOID TAPERING OFF LIPPINGS WHEN FINISHING TO THICKNESS

VENEERS PREPARED IN NORMAL WAY. FACE AND BACKING VENEERS MUST BE PUT ON AT SAME TIME

ENVELOPE SEALED WITH TWO BATTENS AND THREE G CRAMPS

VALVE — TO PUMP

RUBBER ENVELOPE   GROUND

VENEERS   CAULS

BASEBOARD

AIR EVACUATED, VALVE CLOSED, WORK LEFT TO DRY OVERNIGHT OR ACCORDING TO THE SETTING TIME OF THE ADHESIVE USED

NOTE SHEET POLYTHENE IS PLACED BETWEEN THE VENEERS AND CAULS

AFTER SETTING THE WORK IS REMOVED FROM THE ENVELOPE AND THE VENEERS AND GROUND ARE TRIMMED TO THE REQUIRED SIZE

OTHER FORMS OF VACUUM ENVELOPES

POLYTHENE SHEETING MAY BE USED TO FORM AN ENVELOPE — ALSO MANUFACTURED BAGS e.g. GRAIN BAGS

ADVANTAGE   USER CAN SEE THE PROCESS WORKING

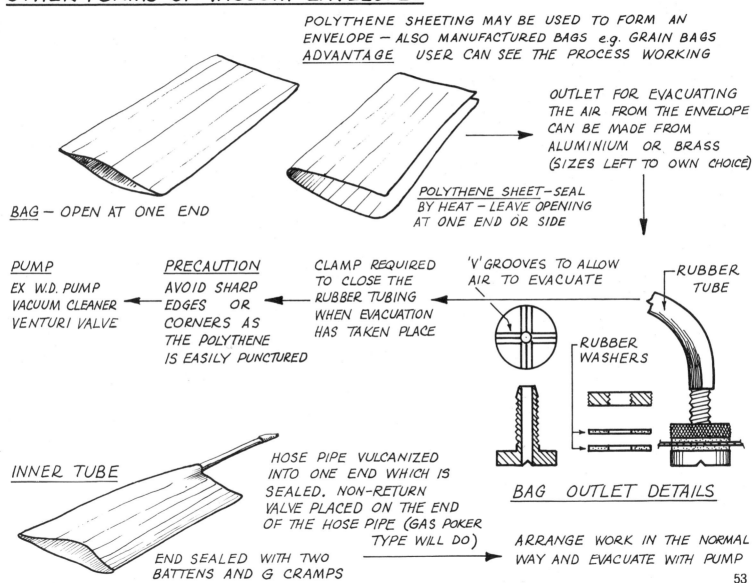

BAG — OPEN AT ONE END

OUTLET FOR EVACUATING THE AIR FROM THE ENVELOPE CAN BE MADE FROM ALUMINIUM OR BRASS (SIZES LEFT TO OWN CHOICE)

POLYTHENE SHEET — SEAL BY HEAT — LEAVE OPENING AT ONE END OR SIDE

PUMP
EX W.D. PUMP
VACUUM CLEANER
VENTURI VALVE

PRECAUTION
AVOID SHARP EDGES OR CORNERS AS THE POLYTHENE IS EASILY PUNCTURED

CLAMP REQUIRED TO CLOSE THE RUBBER TUBING WHEN EVACUATION HAS TAKEN PLACE

'V' GROOVES TO ALLOW AIR TO EVACUATE

RUBBER TUBE

RUBBER WASHERS

BAG OUTLET DETAILS

INNER TUBE

HOSE PIPE VULCANIZED INTO ONE END WHICH IS SEALED. NON-RETURN VALVE PLACED ON THE END OF THE HOSE PIPE (GAS POKER TYPE WILL DO)

END SEALED WITH TWO BATTENS AND G CRAMPS

ARRANGE WORK IN THE NORMAL WAY AND EVACUATE WITH PUMP

TAMBOURS — 1

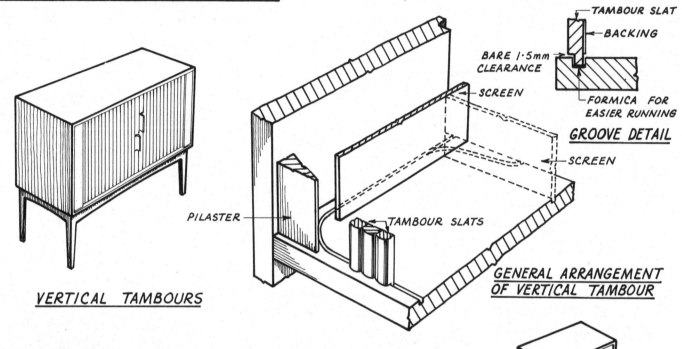

TAMBOUR SLAT

BACKING

BARE 1·5mm
CLEARANCE

FORMICA FOR
EASIER RUNNING

GROOVE DETAIL

SCREEN

SCREEN

PILASTER

TAMBOUR SLATS

VERTICAL TAMBOURS

GENERAL ARRANGEMENT OF VERTICAL TAMBOUR

HORIZONTAL TAMBOUR

CARCASE REQUIREMENTS

1	RUNNING GROOVE – TOP AND BOTTOM
2	ENTRY FOR TAMBOUR AT THE BACK
3	SCREENS – SIDE AND/OR BACK – HOUSED INTO CARCASE
4	PILASTERS

TAMBOUR REQUIREMENTS

1	SLATS OF APPROPRIATE SECTION
2	END TREATMENT – REBATE OR PEGS
3	SUITABLE BACKING MATERIAL – STRONG LINEN OR FINE CANVAS
4	SEPARATE CLOSING SLAT – SUBSEQUENTLY FIXED TO TAMBOUR
5	STOPS – MAY BE FIXED IN THE GROOVES
6	HANDLES – ATTACHED OR SCULPTURED OUT OF CLOSING SLATS

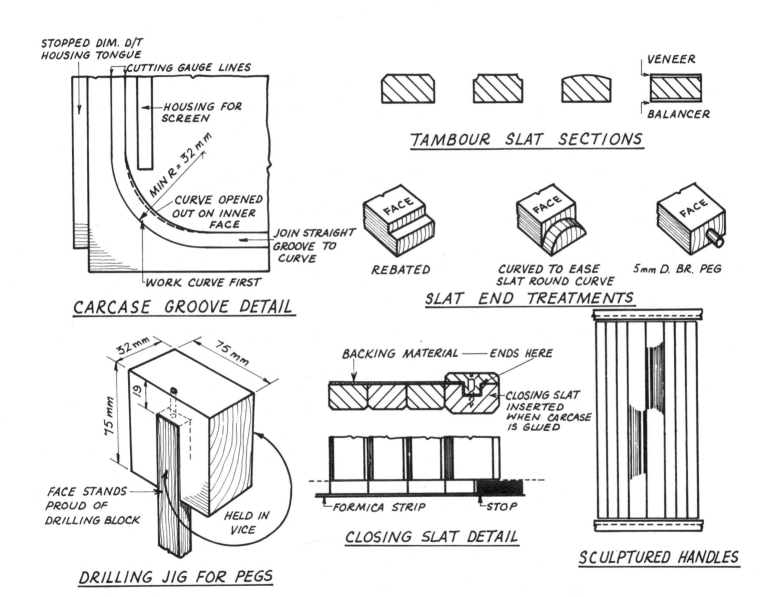

STOPPED DIM. D/T HOUSING TONGUE

CUTTING GAUGE LINES

HOUSING FOR SCREEN

MIN R = 32 mm

CURVE OPENED OUT ON INNER FACE

JOIN STRAIGHT GROOVE TO CURVE

WORK CURVE FIRST

CARCASE GROOVE DETAIL

VENEER

BALANCER

TAMBOUR SLAT SECTIONS

FACE — **REBATED**

FACE — **CURVED TO EASE SLAT ROUND CURVE**

FACE — **5mm D. BR. PEG**

SLAT END TREATMENTS

32 mm   75 mm

19

75 mm

FACE STANDS PROUD OF DRILLING BLOCK

HELD IN VICE

DRILLING JIG FOR PEGS

BACKING MATERIAL — ENDS HERE

CLOSING SLAT INSERTED WHEN CARCASE IS GLUED

FORMICA STRIP   **STOP**

CLOSING SLAT DETAIL

SCULPTURED HANDLES

TAMBOURS — 2

PROCEDURE FOR MAKING TAMBOUR

1. PREPARE THE BOARD FROM WHICH THE SLATS ARE TO BE MADE. SEE FIG. 1.

2. WORK REBATES ALONG THE TOP AND BOTTOM EDGES.

3. RUN OFF THE SLATS, PLUS 3 OR 4 SPARES, ON A FINE TOOTHED CIRCULAR SAW.

4. SHOOT THE EDGES IN A PLANING JIG. SEE FIG 2.

5. WORK THE FACE MOULDING, (FIG. 3) INCLUDING THE CURVING OF THE REBATES IF REQUIRED.

6. CLEAN UP AND POLISH THE FRONT FACES AND EDGES OF ALL THE SLATS.

7. LAY THE SLATS FACE DOWN ON A SHEET OF 19mm BLOCKBOARD AND SECURE ALL ROUND WITH RETAINING STRIPS OF THE SAME THICKNESS AS THE SLATS. FIG. 4.

8. USING A FINE TOOTHING PLANE SURFACE THE BACK FACES OF THE SLATS, HALF THE AREA AT A TIME. THE OTHER HALF BEING HELD DOWN BY A BATTEN SCREWED ACROSS THE SLATS AS SHOWN.

9. COVER THE BACK FACE OF THE SPARE SLAT AT THE CLOSING END, AND A 13mm BAND AT THE TOP AND BOTTOM OF ALL SLATS WITH SELLOTAPE TO PREVENT THE SPREADING OF GLUE WHERE IT IS NOT REQUIRED.

10. CUT THE BACKING CLOTH TO WIDTH AND LEAVE OVERLENGTH.

11. USING VERY HOT THIN SCOTCH GLUE OR P.V.A. GLUE FIX THE BACKING CLOTH FIRMLY. IN POSITION. SEE FIGS 5 & 6. NOTE. IF P.V.A. GLUE IS USED PRESSURE SHOULD BE APPLIED FOR AT LEAST 4 HOURS.

12. WHEN THE GLUE IS DRY CHECK THE ALIGNMENT OF THE REBATED ENDS AND TRUE UP IF NECESSARY.

13. CUT OFF THE SPARE SLAT AT THE BACK END OF THE TAMBOUR.

14. TEST IN THE CARCASE AND FIX BACKING AT THE FRONT END TO THE CLOSING SLAT.

ALTERNATIVE METHOD OF PRODUCING SLATS

1. PREPARE THE MATERIAL AS SHOWN IN FIG. 7.

2. MOULD THE FACE OF EACH SLAT AS REQUIRED. SAW OFF AND PLANE BOTH SAWN FACES. REPEAT AS NECESSARY.

3. FIX DOWN ON BASEBOARD AND WORK REBATES. PROCEDURE IS NOW THE SAME AS FROM NO. 6 ABOVE.

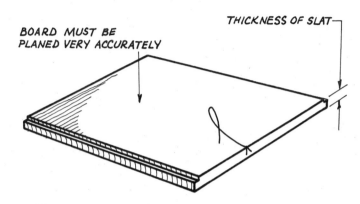

BOARD MUST BE PLANED VERY ACCURATELY

THICKNESS OF SLAT

① MATERIAL READY FOR CUTTING INTO STRIPS

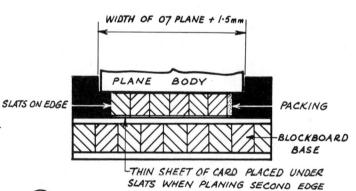

WIDTH OF 07 PLANE + 1.5mm

PLANE BODY

SLATS ON EDGE

PACKING

BLOCKBOARD BASE

THIN SHEET OF CARD PLACED UNDER SLATS WHEN PLANING SECOND EDGE

② SECTIONAL DETAIL OF PLANING JIG

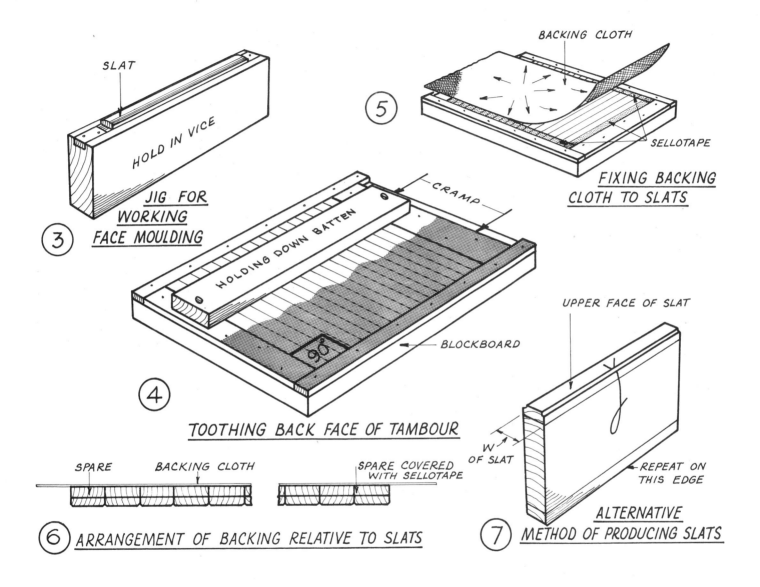

SLAT

HOLD IN VICE

③ JIG FOR WORKING FACE MOULDING

BACKING CLOTH

⑤ SELLOTAPE

FIXING BACKING CLOTH TO SLATS

CRAMP

HOLDING DOWN BATTEN

90°

BLOCKBOARD

④ TOOTHING BACK FACE OF TAMBOUR

UPPER FACE OF SLAT

W OF SLAT

REPEAT ON THIS EDGE

⑦ ALTERNATIVE METHOD OF PRODUCING SLATS

SPARE   BACKING CLOTH   SPARE COVERED WITH SELLOTAPE

⑥ ARRANGEMENT OF BACKING RELATIVE TO SLATS

SIMPLE UPHOLSTERY—1

DROP-IN SEAT USING POLYETHER FOAM

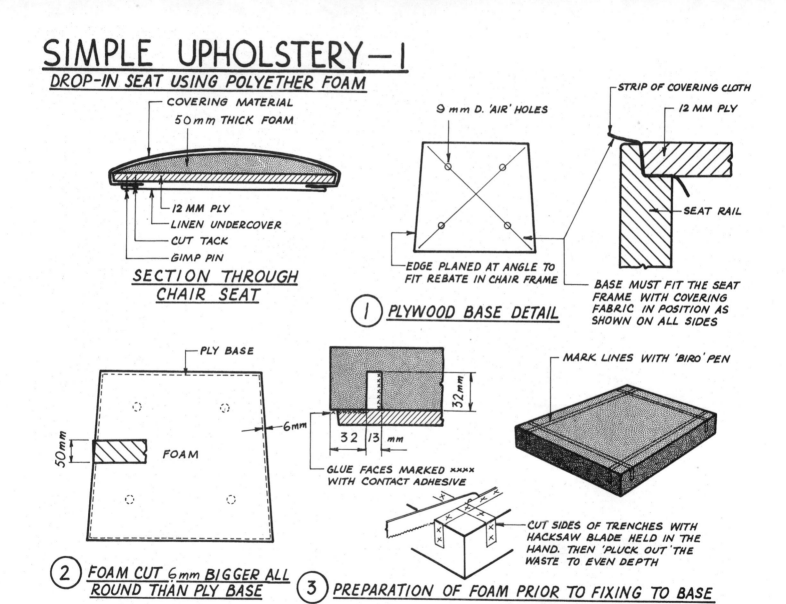

COVERING MATERIAL

50mm THICK FOAM

12 MM PLY
LINEN UNDERCOVER
CUT TACK
GIMP PIN

SECTION THROUGH CHAIR SEAT

9 mm D. 'AIR' HOLES

EDGE PLANED AT ANGLE TO FIT REBATE IN CHAIR FRAME

① **PLYWOOD BASE DETAIL**

STRIP OF COVERING CLOTH

12 MM PLY

SEAT RAIL

BASE MUST FIT THE SEAT FRAME WITH COVERING FABRIC IN POSITION AS SHOWN ON ALL SIDES

PLY BASE

50mm

FOAM

6mm

② **FOAM CUT 6mm BIGGER ALL ROUND THAN PLY BASE**

32mm

32   13   mm

GLUE FACES MARKED ×××× WITH CONTACT ADHESIVE

MARK LINES WITH 'BIRO' PEN

CUT SIDES OF TRENCHES WITH HACKSAW BLADE HELD IN THE HAND. THEN 'PLUCK OUT' THE WASTE TO EVEN DEPTH

③ **PREPARATION OF FOAM PRIOR TO FIXING TO BASE**

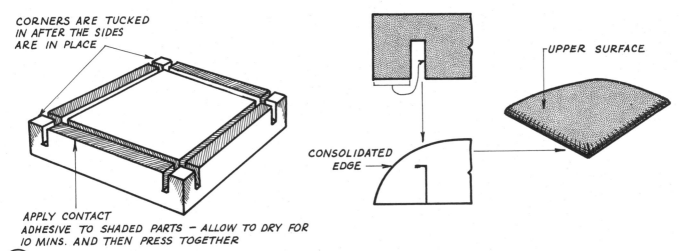

CORNERS ARE TUCKED IN AFTER THE SIDES ARE IN PLACE

UPPER SURFACE

CONSOLIDATED EDGE

APPLY CONTACT ADHESIVE TO SHADED PARTS – ALLOW TO DRY FOR 10 MINS. AND THEN PRESS TOGETHER

④ CONSOLIDATION OF EDGES TO FORM A DURABLE PERIMETER TO THE FOAM BASE

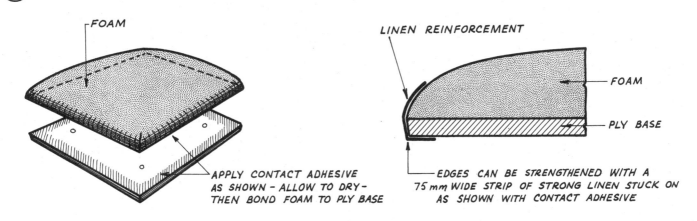

FOAM

LINEN REINFORCEMENT

FOAM

PLY BASE

APPLY CONTACT ADHESIVE AS SHOWN – ALLOW TO DRY – THEN BOND FOAM TO PLY BASE

EDGES CAN BE STRENGTHENED WITH A 75 mm WIDE STRIP OF STRONG LINEN STUCK ON AS SHOWN WITH CONTACT ADHESIVE

⑤ FIXING THE FOAM TO THE PLYWOOD BASE

SIMPLE UPHOLSTERY—2
FIXING FABRIC COVER ONTO THE PREPARED BASE

FRONT EDGE 3 1 2 PULL

PULL

WORK ON A SHEET, OR CLEAN NEWS-PAPER

① FRONT EDGE TACKED ON

CUT TACKS ARE NOT DRIVEN RIGHT HOME AT THIS STAGE

PULL

PULL

VERY STRONG PULL

FABRIC MUST BE TENSIONED EVENLY OVER THE FOAM TO REDUCE THICKNESS TO 25mm AT THE CENTRE

② BACK EDGE TACKED ON

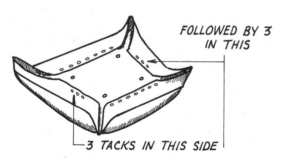

FOLLOWED BY 3 IN THIS

3 TACKS IN THIS SIDE

COMPLETE TACKING SIDES DOWN MAINTAINING EVEN TENSION THROUGHOUT

③ SIDES TACKED DOWN

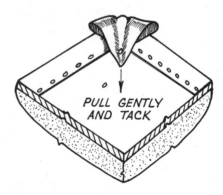

PULL GENTLY AND TACK

④ FIRST STAGE WHEN WORKING A CORNER

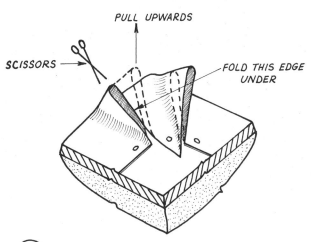

PULL UPWARDS

SCISSORS

FOLD THIS EDGE UNDER

⑤ REMOVING EXCESS MATERIAL AT CORNER

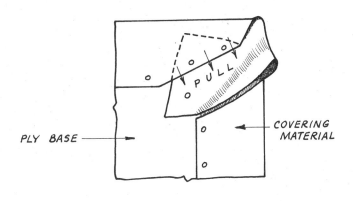

PULL

PLY BASE

COVERING MATERIAL

⑥ FOLD DOWN AND TACK

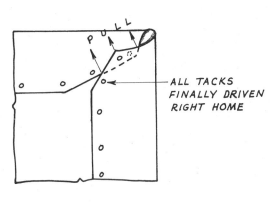

PULL

ALL TACKS FINALLY DRIVEN RIGHT HOME

⑦ FOLD DOWN OTHER SIDE AND TACK

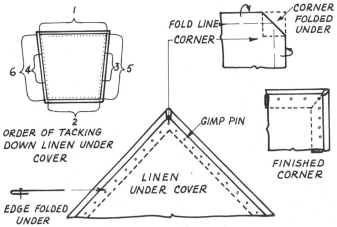

1

6 4   3 5

2

ORDER OF TACKING DOWN LINEN UNDER COVER

FOLD LINE
CORNER

CORNER FOLDED UNDER

GIMP PIN

LINEN UNDER COVER

EDGE FOLDED UNDER

FINISHED CORNER

⑧ FINISHING OFF UNDER SIDE OF CHAIR SEAT

HINGEING —1

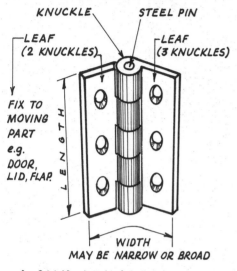

KNUCKLE   STEEL PIN

LEAF (2 KNUCKLES)   LEAF (3 KNUCKLES)

FIX TO MOVING PART e.g. DOOR, LID, FLAP.

LENGTH

WIDTH
MAY BE NARROW OR BROAD

A SOLID DRAWN BRASS BUTT

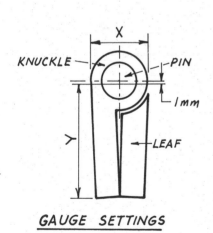

KNUCKLE   PIN

X

1mm

Y

LEAF

GAUGE SETTINGS

(1) THESE EDGES MUST BE PARALLEL

(2) ENDS MUST BE SQUARE

(3)

SCREW HEAD JUST BELOW SURFACE

CHECK HINGES FOR 3 POINTS SHOWN ABOVE

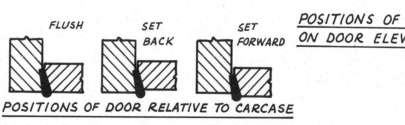

FLUSH   SET BACK   SET FORWARD

POSITIONS OF DOOR RELATIVE TO CARCASE

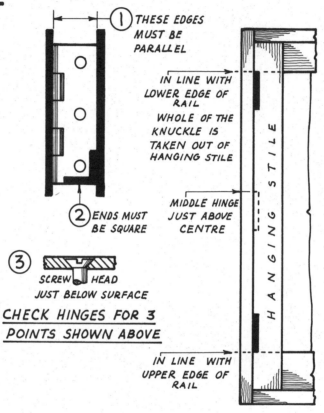

IN LINE WITH LOWER EDGE OF RAIL

WHOLE OF THE KNUCKLE IS TAKEN OUT OF HANGING STILE

MIDDLE HINGE JUST ABOVE CENTRE

HANGING STILE

IN LINE WITH UPPER EDGE OF RAIL

LENGTH OF HINGE

FLUSH DOOR - VENEERED

LENGTH OF HINGE + 9 to 25 mm ACCORDING TO SIZE OF JOB & DISTANCE BELOW EYE LEVEL

POSITIONS OF HINGES ON DOOR ELEVATIONS

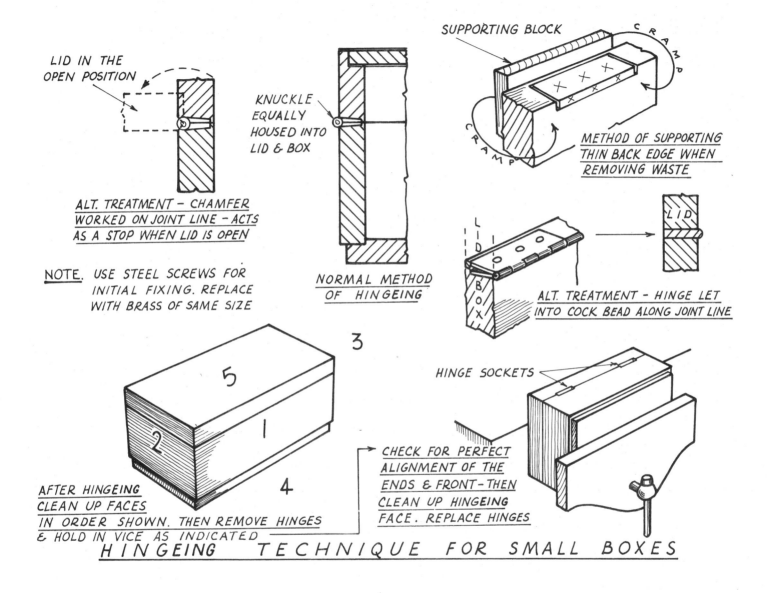

LID IN THE
OPEN POSITION

ALT. TREATMENT – CHAMFER
WORKED ON JOINT LINE – ACTS
AS A STOP WHEN LID IS OPEN

NOTE. USE STEEL SCREWS FOR
INITIAL FIXING. REPLACE
WITH BRASS OF SAME SIZE

KNUCKLE
EQUALLY
HOUSED INTO
LID & BOX

NORMAL METHOD
OF HINGEING

SUPPORTING BLOCK

CRAMP

CRAMP

METHOD OF SUPPORTING
THIN BACK EDGE WHEN
REMOVING WASTE

LID

BOX

LID

ALT. TREATMENT – HINGE LET
INTO COCK BEAD ALONG JOINT LINE

HINGE SOCKETS

AFTER HINGEING
CLEAN UP FACES
IN ORDER SHOWN. THEN REMOVE HINGES
& HOLD IN VICE AS INDICATED

CHECK FOR PERFECT
ALIGNMENT OF THE
ENDS & FRONT – THEN
CLEAN UP HINGEING
FACE. REPLACE HINGES

HINGEING TECHNIQUE FOR SMALL BOXES

HINGEING—2

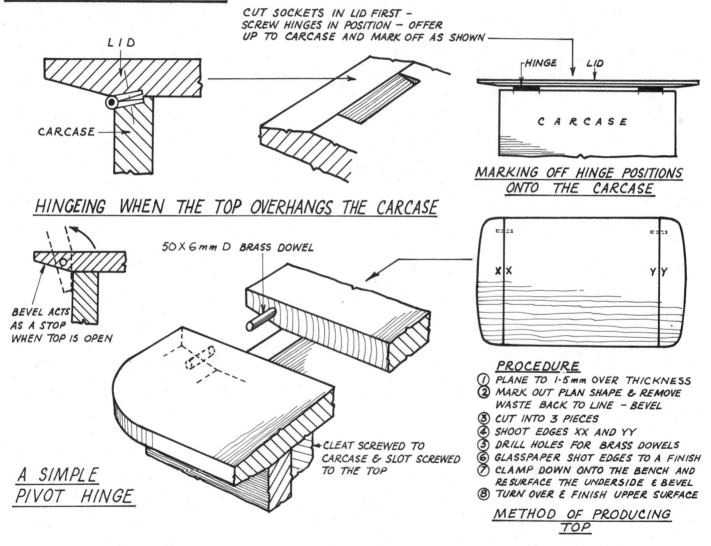

LID

CARCASE

CUT SOCKETS IN LID FIRST —
SCREW HINGES IN POSITION — OFFER
UP TO CARCASE AND MARK OFF AS SHOWN

HINGE   LID

C A R C A S E

MARKING OFF HINGE POSITIONS ONTO THE CARCASE

HINGEING WHEN THE TOP OVERHANGS THE CARCASE

BEVEL ACTS
AS A STOP
WHEN TOP IS OPEN

50 × 6 mm D BRASS DOWEL

X X   Y Y

CLEAT SCREWED TO
CARCASE & SLOT SCREWED
TO THE TOP

A SIMPLE PIVOT HINGE

PROCEDURE

1. PLANE TO 1·5 mm OVER THICKNESS
2. MARK OUT PLAN SHAPE & REMOVE WASTE BACK TO LINE — BEVEL
3. CUT INTO 3 PIECES
4. SHOOT EDGES XX AND YY
5. DRILL HOLES FOR BRASS DOWELS
6. GLASSPAPER SHOT EDGES TO A FINISH
7. CLAMP DOWN ONTO THE BENCH AND RESURFACE THE UNDERSIDE & BEVEL
8. TURN OVER & FINISH UPPER SURFACE

METHOD OF PRODUCING TOP

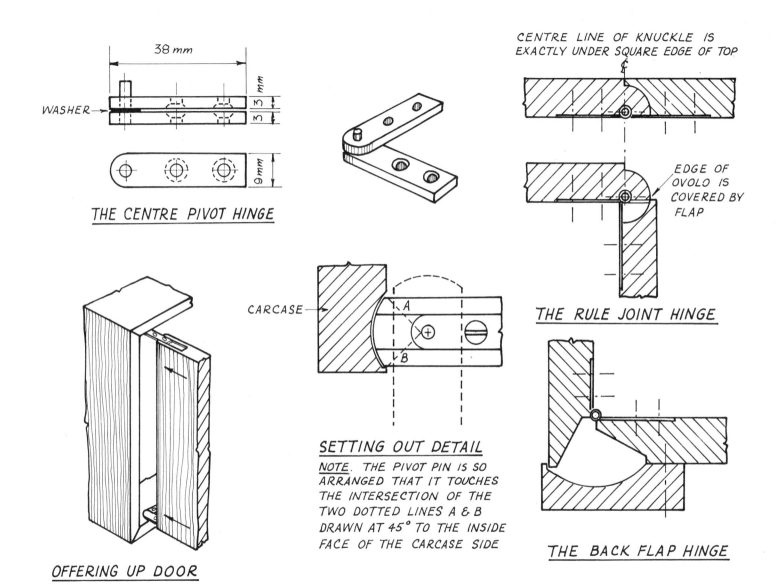

38 mm

WASHER →

3 mm
3 mm
9 mm

THE CENTRE PIVOT HINGE

CENTRE LINE OF KNUCKLE IS
EXACTLY UNDER SQUARE EDGE OF TOP

EDGE OF
OVOLO IS
COVERED BY
FLAP

THE RULE JOINT HINGE

CARCASE →

A
B

SETTING OUT DETAIL

NOTE. THE PIVOT PIN IS SO
ARRANGED THAT IT TOUCHES
THE INTERSECTION OF THE
TWO DOTTED LINES A & B
DRAWN AT 45° TO THE INSIDE
FACE OF THE CARCASE SIDE

OFFERING UP DOOR

THE BACK FLAP HINGE

CABINET FITTINGS — 1

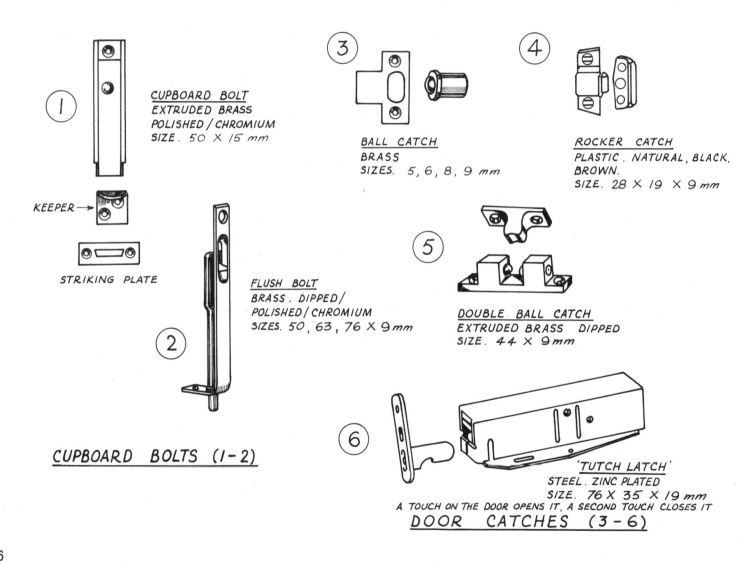

CUPBOARD BOLT
EXTRUDED BRASS
POLISHED / CHROMIUM
SIZE. 50 X 15 mm

KEEPER →

STRIKING PLATE

FLUSH BOLT
BRASS. DIPPED /
/ POLISHED / CHROMIUM
SIZES. 50, 63, 76 X 9 mm

CUPBOARD BOLTS (1-2)

BALL CATCH
BRASS
SIZES. 5, 6, 8, 9 mm

ROCKER CATCH
PLASTIC. NATURAL, BLACK,
BROWN.
SIZE. 28 X 19 X 9 mm

DOUBLE BALL CATCH
EXTRUDED BRASS DIPPED
SIZE. 44 X 9 mm

'TUTCH LATCH'
STEEL. ZINC PLATED
SIZE. 76 X 35 X 19 mm
A TOUCH ON THE DOOR OPENS IT, A SECOND TOUCH CLOSES IT

DOOR CATCHES (3-6)

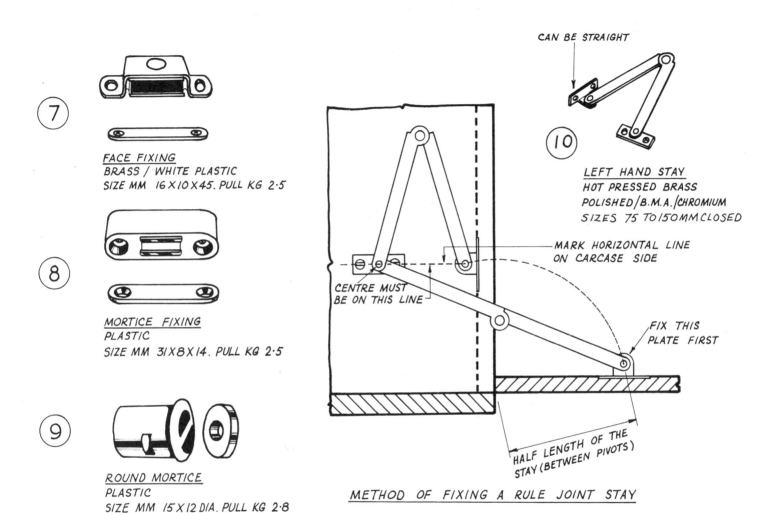

CAN BE STRAIGHT

⑦ FACE FIXING
BRASS / WHITE PLASTIC
SIZE MM 16 X 10 X 45. PULL KG 2·5

⑧ MORTICE FIXING
PLASTIC
SIZE MM 31 X 8 X 14. PULL KG 2·5

⑨ ROUND MORTICE
PLASTIC
SIZE MM 15 X 12 DIA. PULL KG 2·8

⑩ LEFT HAND STAY
HOT PRESSED BRASS
POLISHED / B.M.A. / CHROMIUM
SIZES 75 TO 150 MM CLOSED

MARK HORIZONTAL LINE
ON CARCASE SIDE

CENTRE MUST
BE ON THIS LINE

FIX THIS
PLATE FIRST

HALF LENGTH OF THE
STAY (BETWEEN PIVOTS)

METHOD OF FIXING A RULE JOINT STAY

MAGNETIC CATCHES (7-9)

BUREAU AND CABINET STAY (10)

CABINET FITTINGS — 2 *KNOCK-DOWN TYPES*

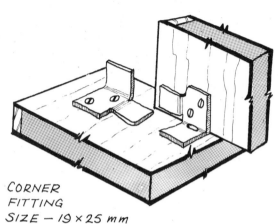

CORNER
FITTING
SIZE — 19 × 25 mm

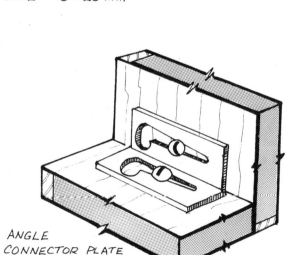

ANGLE
CONNECTOR PLATE
SIZE — 69 × 25 × 19 mm

SELF LOCATING
CAM LOCKING
ACTION

SIZE — 12 × 37 × 25 mm

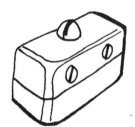

SIZE — 39 × 30 × 16 mm

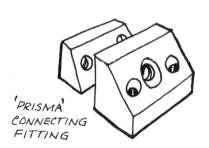

'PRISMA'
CONNECTING
FITTING

TAPER CONNECTOR
SIZES — 100 — 150 mm LONG

KNOCK-DOWN FURNITURE

MODULAR STORAGE UNITS — MANUFACTURED
BY STOREYS OF MORECAMBE, LANCS.

THESE UNITS ARE BUILT FROM HIGH QUALITY CHIPBOARD
FINISHED WITH A TEXTURED VINYL SURFACE IN A
RANGE OF COLOURS. THEY ARE EASILY ASSEMBLED
AND HAVE CONTINENTAL KNOCK-DOWN FITTINGS.

THE MODULAR DESIGN ALLOWS FOR ALTERATION OF THE
PLAN TO SUIT ANY CHANGE IN THE ENVIRONMENT
AND THEY MAY BE ADDED TO AT ANY TIME.

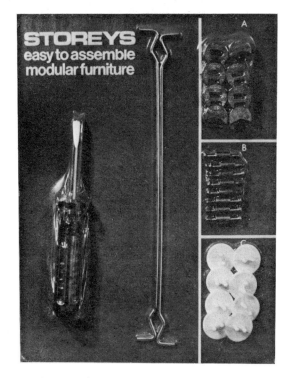

STOREYS
easy to assemble
modular furniture

ASSEMBLY KIT DETAIL

FRAME CONSTRUCTION—I
FRAMES—AS·A BASIS FOR SUPPORTING A SURFACE

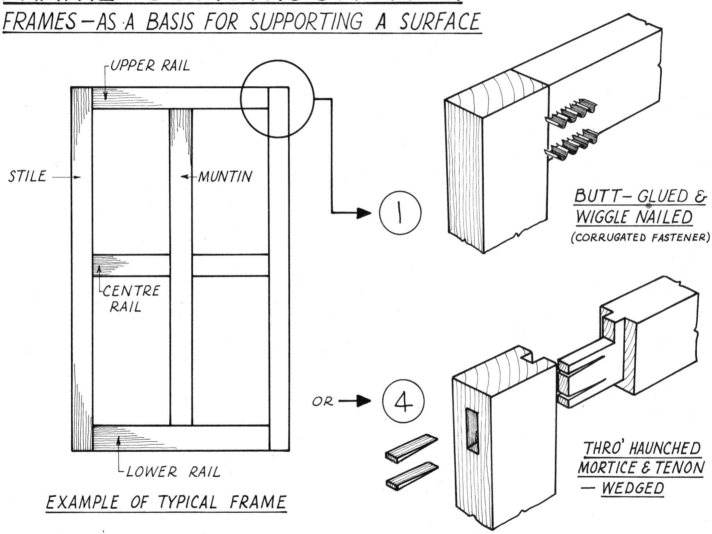

UPPER RAIL

STILE

MUNTIN

CENTRE RAIL

LOWER RAIL

EXAMPLE OF TYPICAL FRAME

①

BUTT- GLUED & WIGGLE NAILED
(CORRUGATED FASTENER)

OR ④

THRO' HAUNCHED MORTICE & TENON — WEDGED

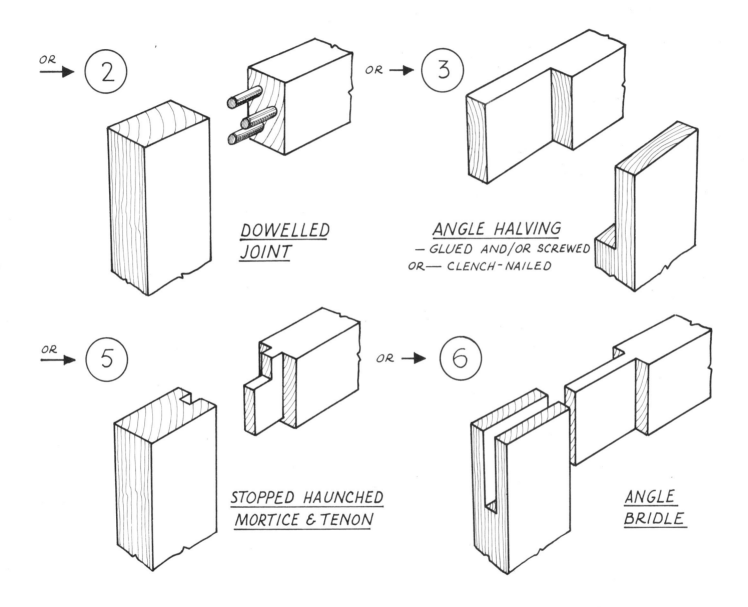

OR → ②

OR → ③

DOWELLED JOINT

ANGLE HALVING
— GLUED AND/OR SCREWED
OR — CLENCH-NAILED

OR → ⑤

OR → ⑥

STOPPED HAUNCHED MORTICE & TENON

ANGLE BRIDLE

FRAME CONSTRUCTION—2
FRAMES—AS A BASE FOR SUPPORTING A SURFACE

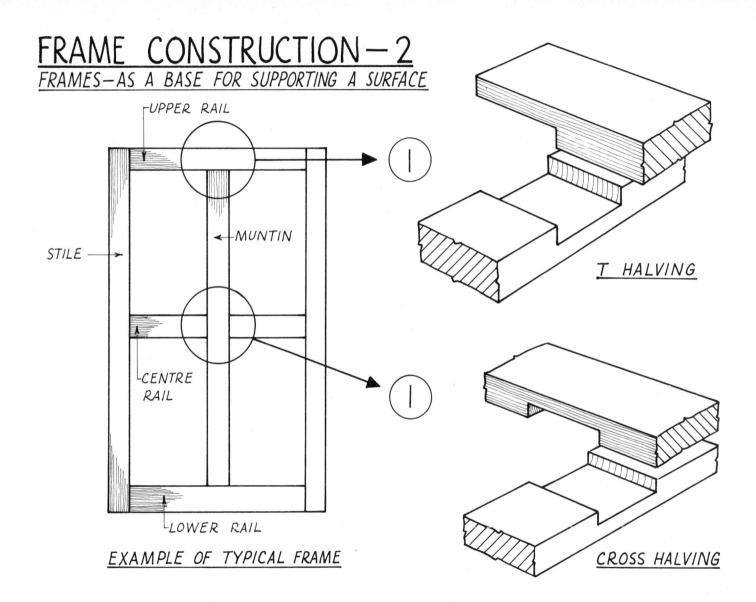

UPPER RAIL

STILE

MUNTIN

CENTRE RAIL

LOWER RAIL

EXAMPLE OF TYPICAL FRAME

T HALVING

CROSS HALVING

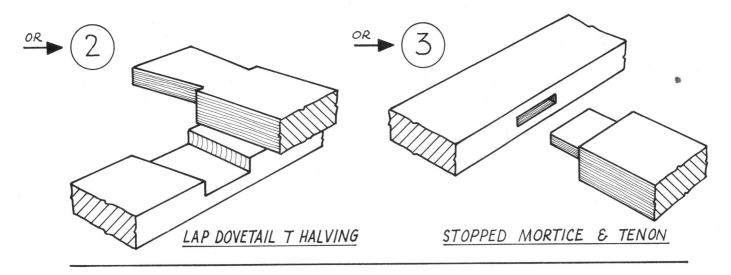

OR → ②

OR → ③

LAP DOVETAIL T HALVING

STOPPED MORTICE & TENON

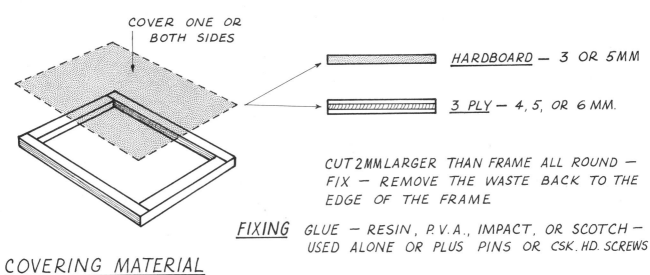

COVER ONE OR
BOTH SIDES

HARDBOARD — 3 OR 5MM

3 PLY — 4, 5, OR 6 MM.

CUT 2MM LARGER THAN FRAME ALL ROUND —
FIX — REMOVE THE WASTE BACK TO THE
EDGE OF THE FRAME

FIXING GLUE — RESIN, P.V.A., IMPACT, OR SCOTCH —
USED ALONE OR PLUS PINS OR CSK. HD. SCREWS

COVERING MATERIAL

FRAME CONSTRUCTION—3

FRAME TO HOLD A PANEL (NOT REMOVABLE) e.g. A DOOR

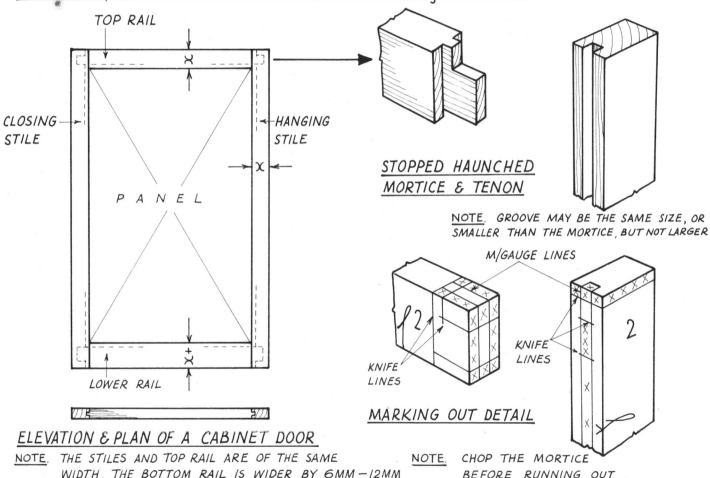

TOP RAIL

CLOSING STILE

HANGING STILE

PANEL

LOWER RAIL

ELEVATION & PLAN OF A CABINET DOOR

NOTE. THE STILES AND TOP RAIL ARE OF THE SAME WIDTH. THE BOTTOM RAIL IS WIDER BY 6MM—12MM DEPENDING ON THE POSITION OF THE DOOR

STOPPED HAUNCHED MORTICE & TENON

NOTE. GROOVE MAY BE THE SAME SIZE, OR SMALLER THAN THE MORTICE, BUT NOT LARGER

M/GAUGE LINES

KNIFE LINES

KNIFE LINES

MARKING OUT DETAIL

NOTE. CHOP THE MORTICE BEFORE RUNNING OUT THE GROOVE

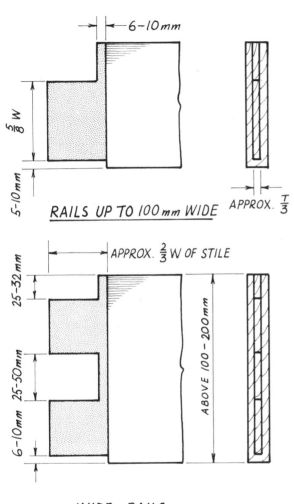

6-10 mm

$\frac{5}{8}$ W

5-10 mm

APPROX. $\frac{T}{3}$

RAILS UP TO 100 mm WIDE

APPROX. $\frac{2}{3}$ W OF STILE

25-32 mm

25-50 mm

6-10 mm

ABOVE 100-200 mm

WIDE RAILS

PROPORTIONS OF TENONS

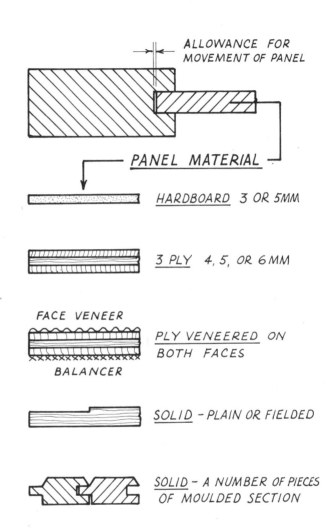

ALLOWANCE FOR MOVEMENT OF PANEL

PANEL MATERIAL

HARDBOARD 3 OR 5MM

3 PLY 4, 5, OR 6MM

FACE VENEER

PLY VENEERED ON BOTH FACES

BALANCER

SOLID - PLAIN OR FIELDED

SOLID - A NUMBER OF PIECES OF MOULDED SECTION

FRAME CONSTRUCTION—4

TYPES OF SOLID PANELS WITHIN FRAMES

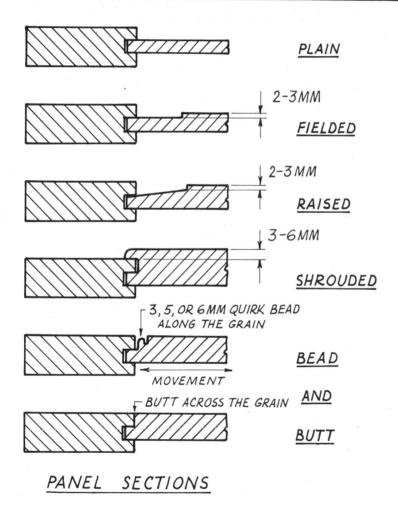

PLAIN

2-3MM

FIELDED

2-3MM

RAISED

3-6MM

SHROUDED

3, 5, OR 6MM QUIRK BEAD
ALONG THE GRAIN

BEAD

MOVEMENT

AND

BUTT ACROSS THE GRAIN

BUTT

PANEL SECTIONS

NOTES.

1. PANELS SHOULD BE A SNUG FIT IN THE GROOVES CONTAINING THEM.

2. THEY SHOULD BE SLIGHTLY SMALLER THAN THE FRAMES TO ALLOW FOR MOVEMENT AFTER MAKING UP.

3. PANELS MUST NOT BE GLUED INTO THE FRAMES.

4. PANEL SURFACES WHICH ARE BELOW THOSE OF THE FRAME CONTAINING THEM SHOULD BE CLEANED UP AND POLISHED BEFORE ASSEMBLY.

5. THE QUIRK BEAD SHOULD BE RUN OUT SO THAT IT IS AT LEAST 1MM BELOW THE PANEL SURFACE. IT SHOULD BE POLISHED BEFORE ASSEMBLY.

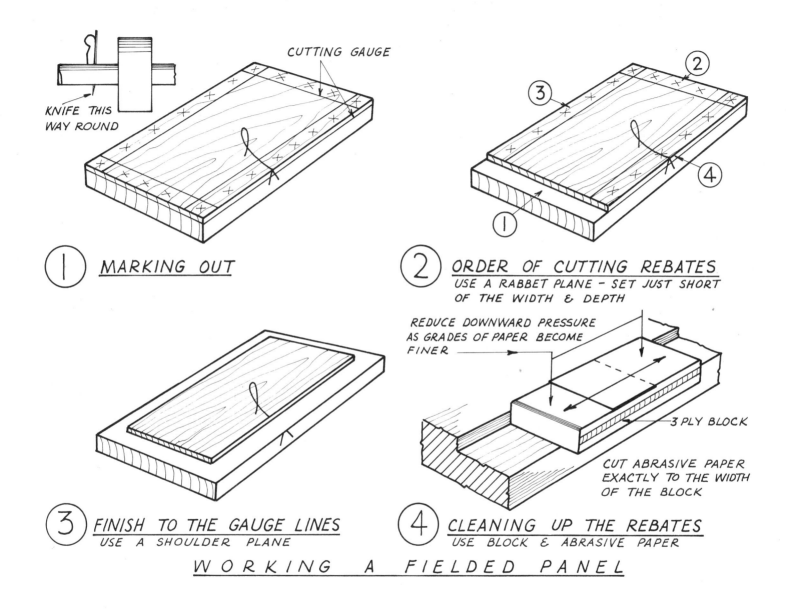

CUTTING GAUGE

KNIFE THIS WAY ROUND

① **MARKING OUT**

② **ORDER OF CUTTING REBATES**
USE A RABBET PLANE - SET JUST SHORT OF THE WIDTH & DEPTH

③ **FINISH TO THE GAUGE LINES**
USE A SHOULDER PLANE

REDUCE DOWNWARD PRESSURE AS GRADES OF PAPER BECOME FINER

3 PLY BLOCK

CUT ABRASIVE PAPER EXACTLY TO THE WIDTH OF THE BLOCK

④ **CLEANING UP THE REBATES**
USE BLOCK & ABRASIVE PAPER

WORKING A FIELDED PANEL

FRAME CONSTRUCTION—5

FRAMES TO HOLD A REMOVABLE PANEL (REBATED)

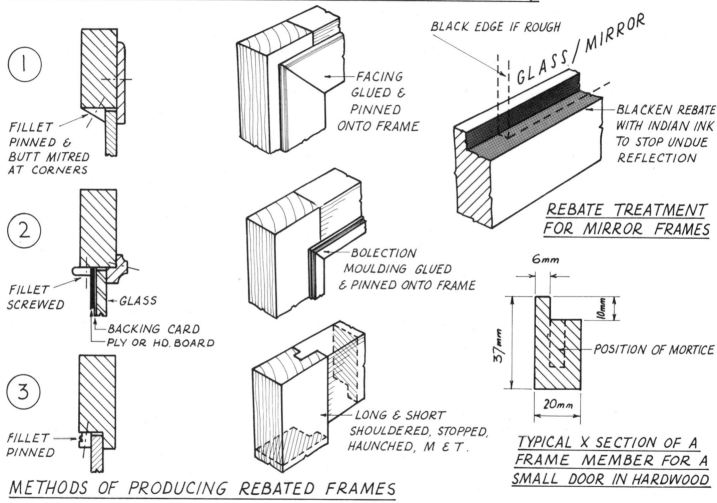

① FILLET PINNED & BUTT MITRED AT CORNERS

② FILLET SCREWED
— GLASS
— BACKING CARD
PLY OR HD. BOARD

③ FILLET PINNED

METHODS OF PRODUCING REBATED FRAMES

FACING GLUED & PINNED ONTO FRAME

BOLECTION MOULDING GLUED & PINNED ONTO FRAME

LONG & SHORT SHOULDERED, STOPPED, HAUNCHED, M & T.

BLACK EDGE IF ROUGH

GLASS / MIRROR

BLACKEN REBATE WITH INDIAN INK TO STOP UNDUE REFLECTION

REBATE TREATMENT FOR MIRROR FRAMES

6mm
10mm
37mm
20mm

POSITION OF MORTICE

TYPICAL X SECTION OF A FRAME MEMBER FOR A SMALL DOOR IN HARDWOOD

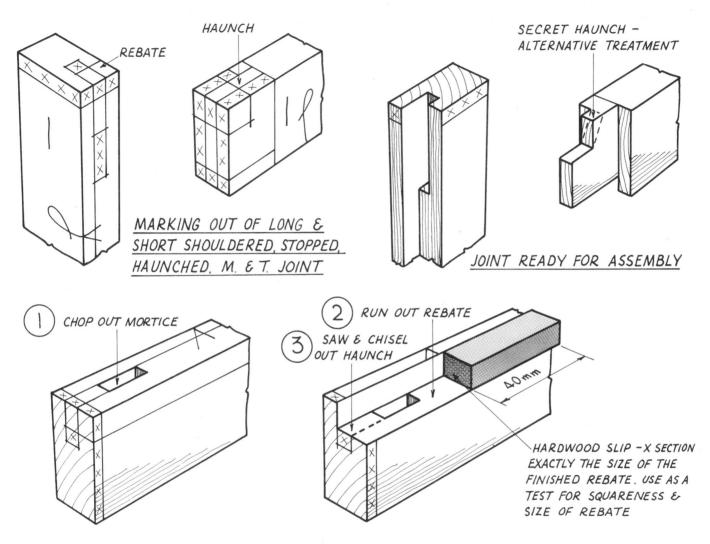

REBATE

HAUNCH

MARKING OUT OF LONG &
SHORT SHOULDERED, STOPPED,
HAUNCHED, M. & T. JOINT

SECRET HAUNCH –
ALTERNATIVE TREATMENT

JOINT READY FOR ASSEMBLY

① CHOP OUT MORTICE

② RUN OUT REBATE

③ SAW & CHISEL
OUT HAUNCH

40 mm

HARDWOOD SLIP – X SECTION
EXACTLY THE SIZE OF THE
FINISHED REBATE. USE AS A
TEST FOR SQUARENESS &
SIZE OF REBATE

STAGES OF REMOVING WASTE FROM THE STILE

FRAME CONSTRUCTION—6
FRAMES REQUIRING INTERNAL SHAPING

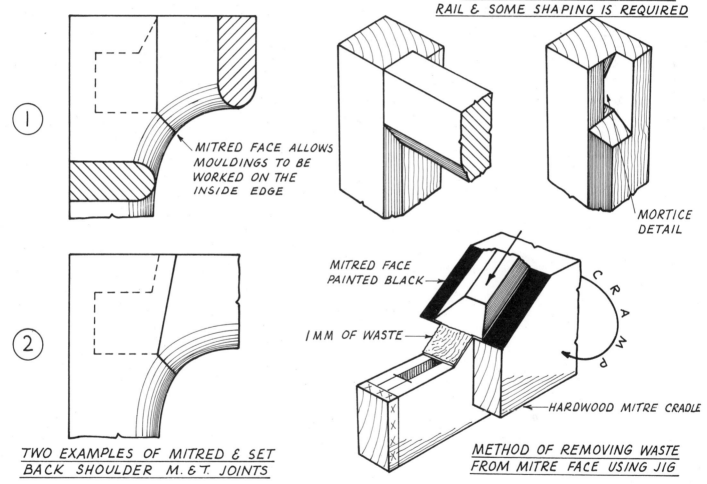

① MITRED FACE ALLOWS
MOULDINGS TO BE
WORKED ON THE
INSIDE EDGE

MORTICE
DETAIL

② TWO EXAMPLES OF MITRED & SET
BACK SHOULDER M. & T. JOINTS

MITRED FACE
PAINTED BLACK

1MM OF WASTE

CRAMP

HARDWOOD MITRE CRADLE

METHOD OF REMOVING WASTE
FROM MITRE FACE USING JIG

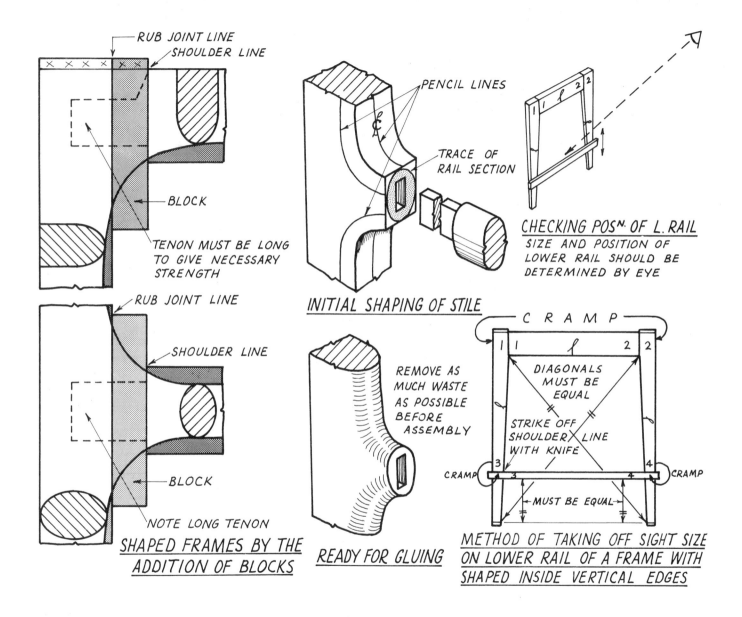

RUB JOINT LINE
SHOULDER LINE

× × × × × × × ×

BLOCK

TENON MUST BE LONG
TO GIVE NECESSARY
STRENGTH

RUB JOINT LINE

SHOULDER LINE

BLOCK

NOTE LONG TENON

SHAPED FRAMES BY THE
ADDITION OF BLOCKS

PENCIL LINES

℄

TRACE OF
RAIL SECTION

INITIAL SHAPING OF STILE

REMOVE AS
MUCH WASTE
AS POSSIBLE
BEFORE
ASSEMBLY

READY FOR GLUING

CHECKING POSⁿ. OF L. RAIL
SIZE AND POSITION OF
LOWER RAIL SHOULD BE
DETERMINED BY EYE

C R A M P

1 1   ℓ   2 2

DIAGONALS
MUST BE
EQUAL

STRIKE OFF
SHOULDER LINE
WITH KNIFE

3   3   4   4

CRAMP   CRAMP

MUST BE EQUAL

METHOD OF TAKING OFF SIGHT SIZE
ON LOWER RAIL OF A FRAME WITH
SHAPED INSIDE VERTICAL EDGES

FRAME CONSTRUCTION-7
BACK FRAMES USED IN GOOD CABINET WORK

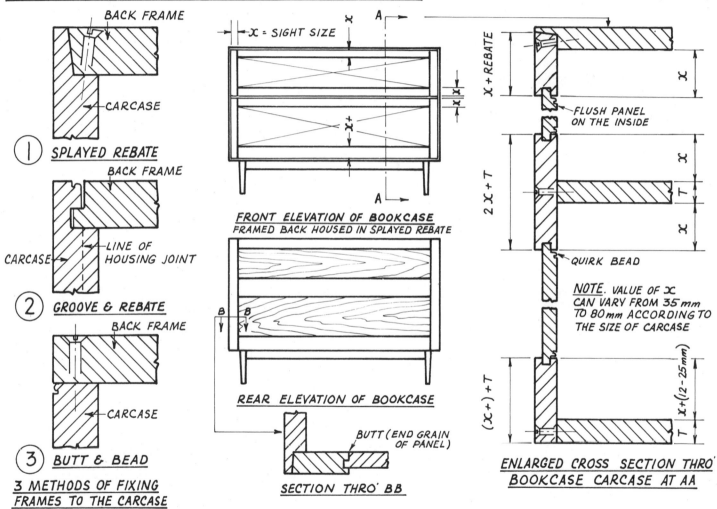

BACK FRAME

CARCASE

① **SPLAYED REBATE**

BACK FRAME

CARCASE

LINE OF HOUSING JOINT

② **GROOVE & REBATE**

BACK FRAME

CARCASE

③ **BUTT & BEAD**

3 METHODS OF FIXING FRAMES TO THE CARCASE

x = SIGHT SIZE

A

x

$x+$

A

FRONT ELEVATION OF BOOKCASE
FRAMED BACK HOUSED IN SPLAYED REBATE

B   B

REAR ELEVATION OF BOOKCASE

BUTT (END GRAIN OF PANEL)

SECTION THRO' BB

A

$X + REBATE$

FLUSH PANEL ON THE INSIDE

$2X + T$

x

T

x

QUIRK BEAD

<u>NOTE</u>. VALUE OF x CAN VARY FROM 35 mm TO 80 mm ACCORDING TO THE SIZE OF CARCASE

$(X+) + T$

$X + (12 - 25mm)$

T

ENLARGED CROSS SECTION THRO' BOOKCASE CARCASE AT AA

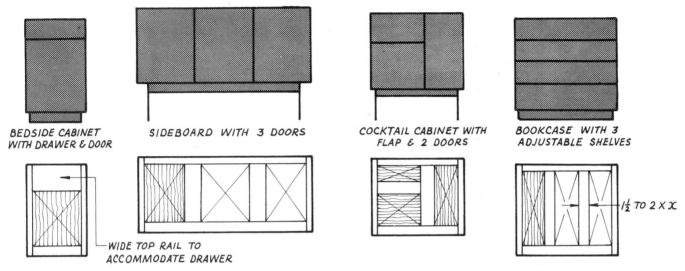

BEDSIDE CABINET
WITH DRAWER & DOOR

SIDEBOARD WITH 3 DOORS

COCKTAIL CABINET WITH
FLAP & 2 DOORS

BOOKCASE WITH 3
ADJUSTABLE SHELVES

WIDE TOP RAIL TO
ACCOMMODATE DRAWER

$1\frac{1}{2}$ TO $2 \times x$

BACK FRAME TREATMENTS FOR EXAMPLES SHOWN ABOVE

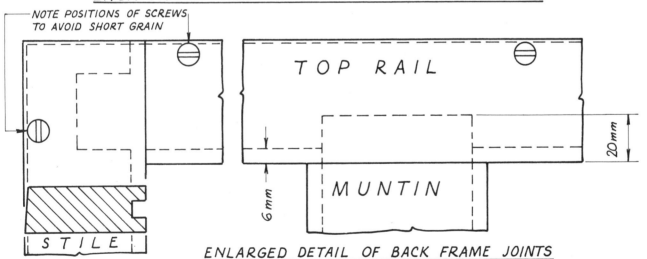

NOTE POSITIONS OF SCREWS
TO AVOID SHORT GRAIN

TOP RAIL

MUNTIN

STILE

20mm

6mm

ENLARGED DETAIL OF BACK FRAME JOINTS

FRAME CONSTRUCTION—8

PICTURE FRAMES

BUILT UP

EXAMPLES OF PICTURE FRAME SECTIONS

NOTE HOW THE SHORT FRAME MEMBER
IS SET UP SO THAT WHEN THE PIN IS
DRIVEN HOME THE JOINT WILL SLIDE DOWN
INTO POSITION

APPROX 2 MM

HAMMER

HELD IN THE VICE

JOINING THE SHORT
TO THE LONG SIDE

HELD IN
THE HAND

NOTE. IF A FINE SAW IS USED THE JOINT
FACES MAY BE LEFT AS CUT

PLANE

MITRE BOX

MITRE SHOOTING BOARD
FOR SMALL MOULDINGS

CUTTING FRAME MEMBERS TO LENGTH

GLUE IS APPLIED SPARINGLY TO SHADED AREA
ONLY. WHEN JOINT IS MADE THE GLUE WILL
SPREAD OVER THE COMPLETE AREA BUT NOT
EXUDE ONTO THE TOP FACE

GLUING DETAIL

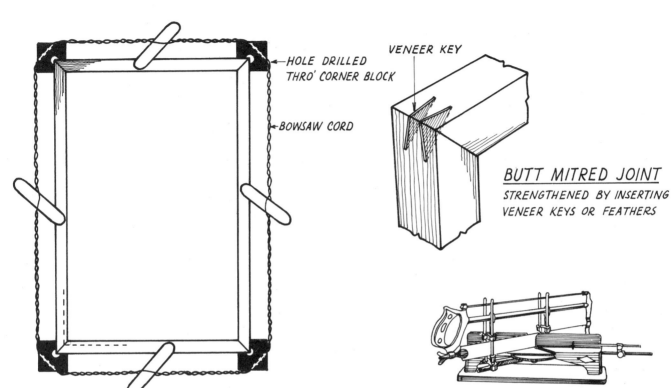

HOLE DRILLED
THRO' CORNER BLOCK

BOWSAW CORD

VENEER KEY

BUTT MITRED JOINT
STRENGTHENED BY INSERTING
VENEER KEYS OR FEATHERS

TOURNIQUET METHOD OF CRAMPING FRAME

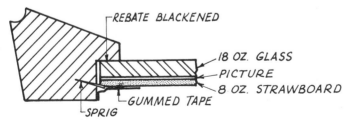

REBATE BLACKENED

18 OZ. GLASS
PICTURE
8 OZ. STRAWBOARD
GUMMED TAPE
SPRIG

SECTION THRO' PICTURE FRAME SHOWING
HOW CONTENTS MAY BE HELD IN PLACE

'ULMIA' MITRE SAW

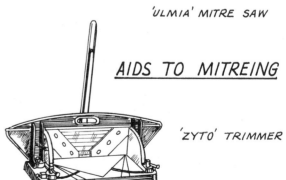

AIDS TO MITREING

'ZYTO' TRIMMER

CARCASE CONSTRUCTION—1

SMALL BOXES

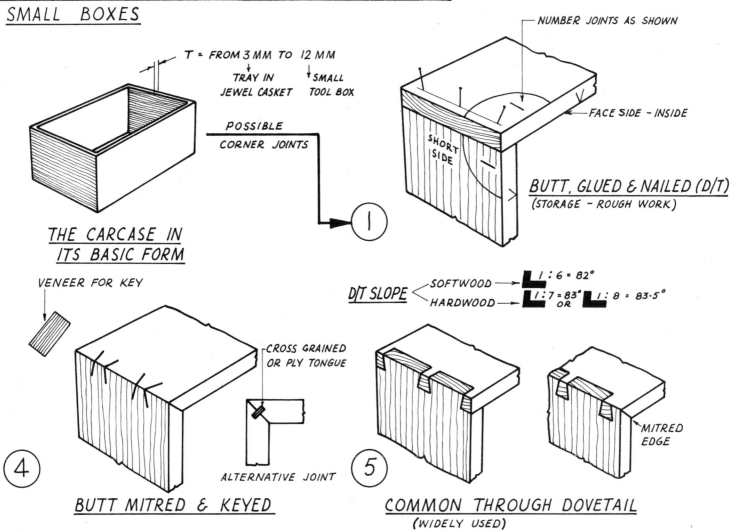

T = FROM 3 MM TO 12 MM

TRAY IN JEWEL CASKET

SMALL TOOL BOX

POSSIBLE CORNER JOINTS

THE CARCASE IN ITS BASIC FORM

NUMBER JOINTS AS SHOWN

SHORT SIDE

FACE SIDE – INSIDE

BUTT, GLUED & NAILED (D/T)
(STORAGE – ROUGH WORK)

VENEER FOR KEY

CROSS GRAINED OR PLY TONGUE

ALTERNATIVE JOINT

BUTT MITRED & KEYED

D/T SLOPE — SOFTWOOD → 1 : 6 = 82°

HARDWOOD → 1 : 7 = 83° OR 1 : 8 = 83.5°

MITRED EDGE

COMMON THROUGH DOVETAIL
(WIDELY USED)

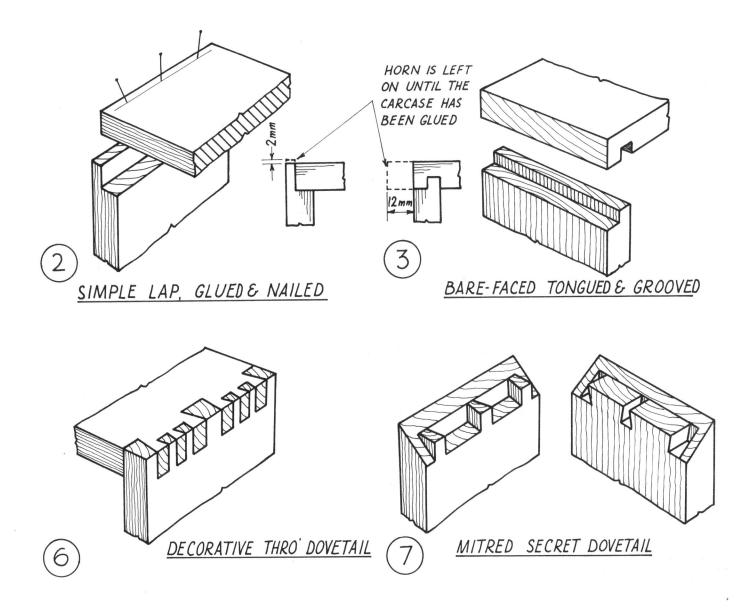

HORN IS LEFT ON UNTIL THE CARCASE HAS BEEN GLUED

2mm

12mm

② SIMPLE LAP, GLUED & NAILED

③ BARE-FACED TONGUED & GROOVED

⑥ DECORATIVE THRO' DOVETAIL

⑦ MITRED SECRET DOVETAIL

CARCASE CONSTRUCTION—2

SMALL BOXES   TOPS, BASES, & LININGS

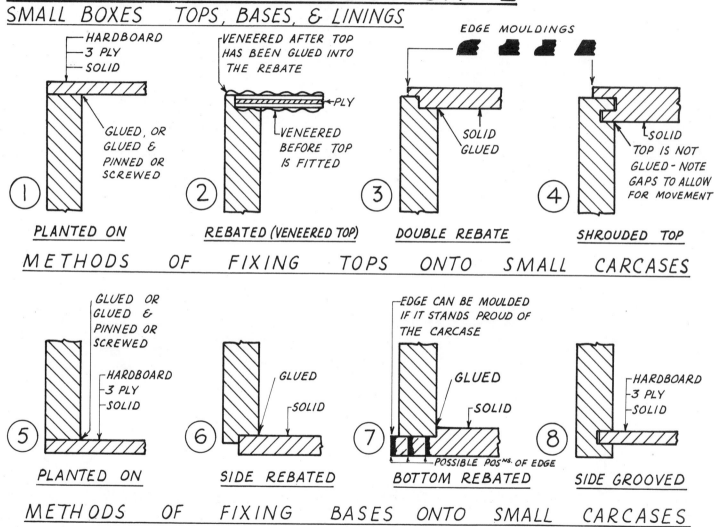

HARDBOARD
3 PLY
SOLID

GLUED, OR
GLUED &
PINNED OR
SCREWED

① **PLANTED ON**

VENEERED AFTER TOP
HAS BEEN GLUED INTO
THE REBATE

PLY

VENEERED
BEFORE TOP
IS FITTED

② **REBATED (VENEERED TOP)**

EDGE MOULDINGS

SOLID
GLUED

③ **DOUBLE REBATE**

SOLID
TOP IS NOT
GLUED - NOTE
GAPS TO ALLOW
FOR MOVEMENT

④ **SHROUDED TOP**

METHODS   OF   FIXING   TOPS   ONTO   SMALL   CARCASES

GLUED OR
GLUED &
PINNED OR
SCREWED

HARDBOARD
3 PLY
SOLID

⑤ **PLANTED ON**

GLUED

SOLID

⑥ **SIDE REBATED**

EDGE CAN BE MOULDED
IF IT STANDS PROUD OF
THE CARCASE

GLUED

SOLID

POSSIBLE POSᴺˢ. OF EDGE

⑦ **BOTTOM REBATED**

HARDBOARD
3 PLY
SOLID

⑧ **SIDE GROOVED**

METHODS   OF   FIXING   BASES   ONTO   SMALL   CARCASES

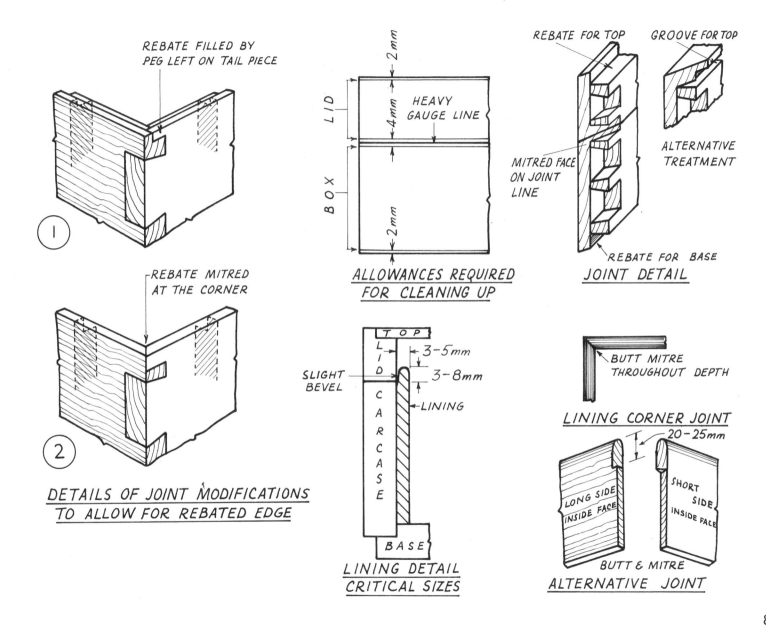

REBATE FILLED BY
PEG LEFT ON TAIL PIECE

①

REBATE MITRED
AT THE CORNER

②

DETAILS OF JOINT MODIFICATIONS
TO ALLOW FOR REBATED EDGE

LID

BOX

2 mm

4 mm

2 mm

HEAVY
GAUGE LINE

ALLOWANCES REQUIRED
FOR CLEANING UP

REBATE FOR TOP

GROOVE FOR TOP

MITRED FACE
ON JOINT
LINE

REBATE FOR BASE

ALTERNATIVE
TREATMENT

JOINT DETAIL

TOP

LID

LID
CARCASE

BASE

3-5mm

3-8mm

SLIGHT
BEVEL

LINING

LINING DETAIL
CRITICAL SIZES

BUTT MITRE
THROUGHOUT DEPTH

LINING CORNER JOINT

20-25mm

LONG SIDE
INSIDE FACE

SHORT
SIDE
INSIDE FACE

BUTT & MITRE
ALTERNATIVE JOINT

CARCASE CONSTRUCTION–3
NORMAL CABINET CONSTRUCTION USING SOLID TIMBER

TAILS ON HORIZONTAL MEMBER

A

B

PINS ON
VERTICAL MEMBER

FREE STANDING CARCASE

T VARIES FROM 12 – 22 MM

12 MM SMALL HANGING CABINET

16 MM BEDSIDE CABINET

20 MM MED. SIZED BOOKCASE, SIDEBOARD,
BUREAU, COCKTAIL CABINET
22 MM LARGE BOOKCASES, SIDEBOARDS,
AND WARDROBES

WALL

TAILS ON VERTICAL
MEMBER

PINS ON
HORIZONTAL
MEMBER

HANGING CARCASE

BASIC CARCASE JOINTS ARE INFLUENCED BY :-
1. TYPE OF BACK
2. FRONT TREATMENT
3. STRESSES IMPOSED ON THE JOINTS
4. WIDTH OF THE BOARDS USED

POSSIBLE VARIATIONS OF THE CORNER JOINTS

A			B		
	1	COMMON THROUGH DOVETAIL		1	COMMON THROUGH DOVETAIL
	2	LAP DOVETAIL		2	LAP DOVETAIL
	3	DECORATIVE THROUGH DOVETAIL		3	DECORATIVE THROUGH DOVETAIL
	4	SECRET OR DOUBLE LAPPED DOVETAIL			
	5	SECRET MITRED DOVETAIL			

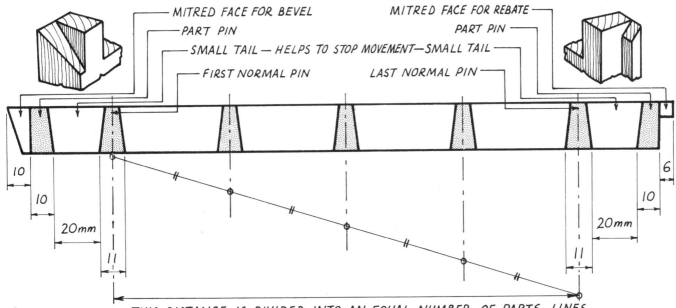

MITRED FACE FOR BEVEL —   MITRED FACE FOR REBATE
PART PIN —   PART PIN
SMALL TAIL — HELPS TO STOP MOVEMENT — SMALL TAIL
FIRST NORMAL PIN —   LAST NORMAL PIN

10   6
10   10
20mm   20mm
11   11

THIS DISTANCE IS DIVIDED INTO AN EQUAL NUMBER OF PARTS. LINES
ARE THEN PROJECTED UPWARDS TO GIVE THE CENTRE LINES OF THE REMAINING PINS. THE NUMBER
OF TAILS BETWEEN THE FIRST AND LAST NORMAL PINS DEPENDS ON THE WIDTH OF THE CARCASE, BUT THE
ROOT OF THE TAIL SHOULD NOT BE SMALLER THAN TWICE THE WIDTH OF THE PIN OR EXCEED 40 MM.

SUGGESTED PROCEDURE

1. DRAW FULL SIZE A RECTANGLE TO REPRESENT A PLAN VIEW OF THE CARCASE MEMBER.
2. DRAW BOTH EDGES AS REQUIRED. E.G. A BEVEL ON THE FRONT AND A REBATE ON THE BACK.
3. WORK OUT THE FRONT DETAIL UP TO AND INCLUDING THE FIRST NORMAL PIN.
4. WORK OUT THE REAR DETAIL UP TO AND INCLUDING THE LAST NORMAL PIN.
5. DIVIDE THE DISTANCE BETWEEN THE CENTRE LINES OF THE FIRST AND LAST NORMAL PINS INTO
   AN EQUAL NUMBER OF PARTS ACCORDING TO THE NUMBER OF TAILS REQUIRED.
6. PRODUCE CENTRE LINES ONTO THE PLAN VIEW AND BALANCE THE PINS ABOUT THEM.

DESIGNING A THROUGH DOVETAIL JOINT FOR A CARCASE 280MM WIDE

CARCASE CONSTRUCTION — 4

EXAMPLE. CARCASE WITH COMMON THROUGH DOVETAILS AT ALL CORNERS — MITRED ON THE FRONT EDGE & REBATED AT THE BACK

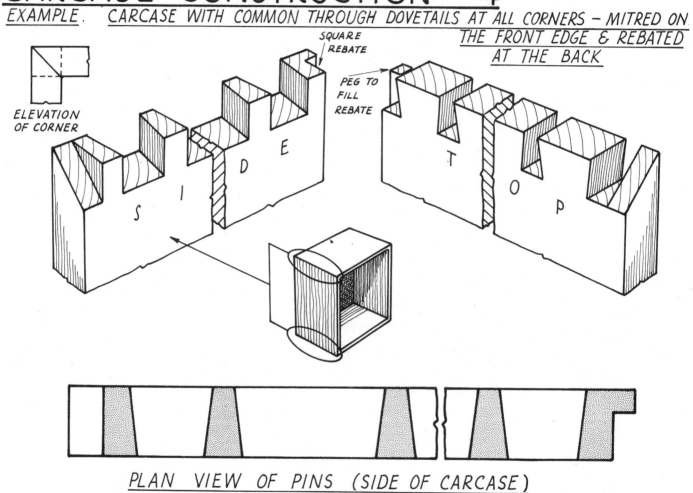

ELEVATION OF CORNER

SQUARE REBATE

PEG TO FILL REBATE

S I D E

T O P

PLAN VIEW OF PINS (SIDE OF CARCASE)

92

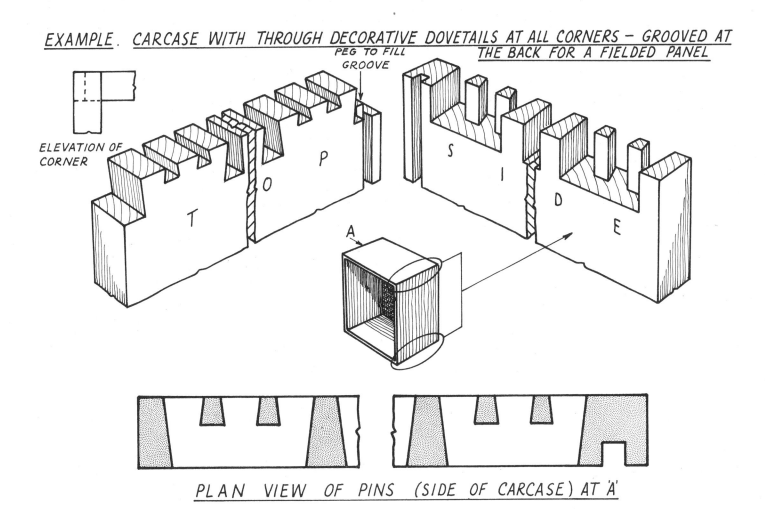

ELEVATION OF CORNER

PEG TO FILL GROOVE

T O P

S I D E

A

PLAN VIEW OF PINS (SIDE OF CARCASE) AT 'A'

CARCASE CONSTRUCTION-5

EXAMPLE   _CARCASE WITH SECRET LAP DOVETAIL AT TOP – GROOVED FOR GLASS_
DOORS & WITH REBATED
BACK EDGE FOR FRAMED
& PANELLED BACK

SPLAYED
REBATE

S I D E

T O P

CLOSING GROOVE
FOR GLASS – ONE
EACH SIDE

GROOVES OF DOUBLE
DEPTH TO ALLOW ENTRY
& REMOVAL OF GLASS

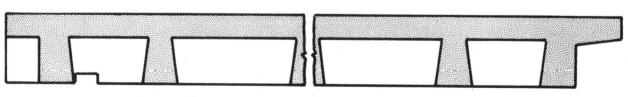

PLAN VIEW OF PINS (SIDE OF CARCASE)

LAP DOVETAIL JOINT AT THE BOTTOM

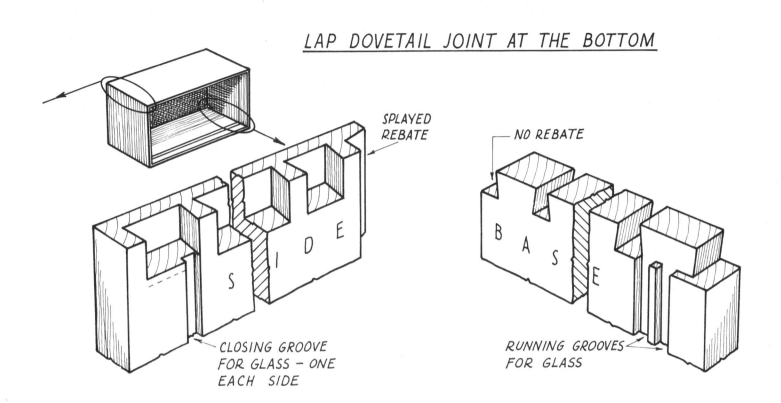

SPLAYED
REBATE

NO REBATE

S I D E

B A S E

CLOSING GROOVE
FOR GLASS — ONE
EACH SIDE

RUNNING GROOVES
FOR GLASS

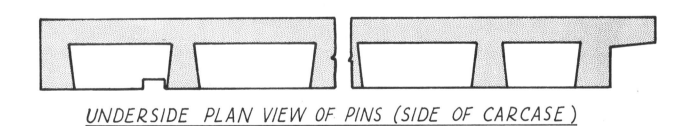

UNDERSIDE PLAN VIEW OF PINS (SIDE OF CARCASE)

CARCASE CONSTRUCTION—6

EXAMPLE. CARCASE WITH SECRET OR DOUBLE LAP DOVETAILS AT THE TOP & LAP DOVETAILS AT THE BOTTOM. MITRED AT THE TOP FRONT CORNERS & REBATED AT THE BACK

ELEV. OF FRONT
TOP CORNER

T O P

S I D E

SPLAYED REBATE

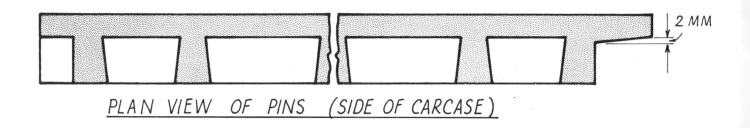

2 MM

PLAN VIEW OF PINS (SIDE OF CARCASE)

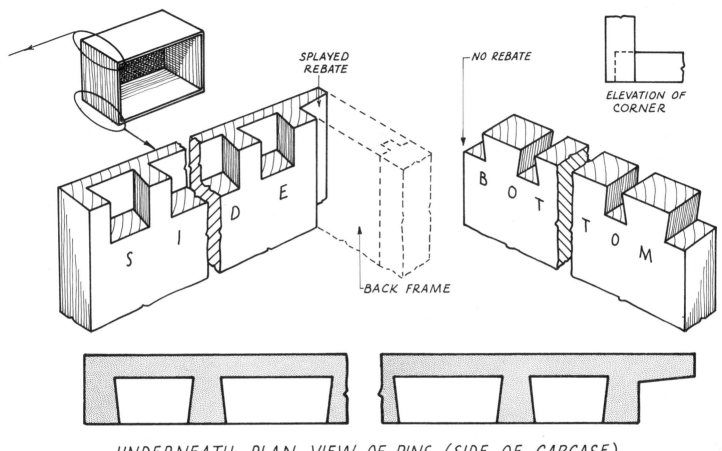

SPLAYED REBATE

NO REBATE

ELEVATION OF CORNER

SIDE

BOTTOM

BACK FRAME

UNDERNEATH PLAN VIEW OF PINS (SIDE OF CARCASE)

CARCASE CONSTRUCTION—7

EXAMPLE   CARCASE WITH SECRET MITRED DOVETAILS AT THE TOP & LAP DOVETAILS AT THE BOTTOM. MITRED AT THE TOP FRONT CORNERS & GROOVED AT THE BACK

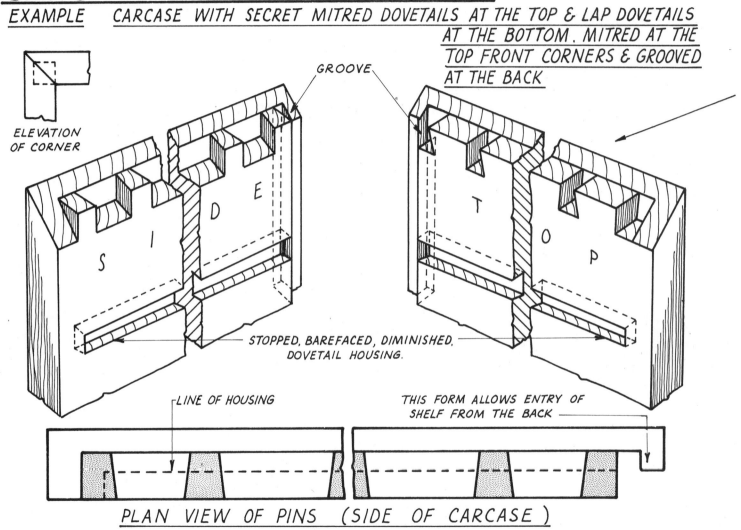

ELEVATION OF CORNER

GROOVE

SIDE

S I D E

TOP

T O P

STOPPED, BAREFACED, DIMINISHED, DOVETAIL HOUSING.

LINE OF HOUSING

THIS FORM ALLOWS ENTRY OF SHELF FROM THE BACK

PLAN VIEW OF PINS (SIDE OF CARCASE)

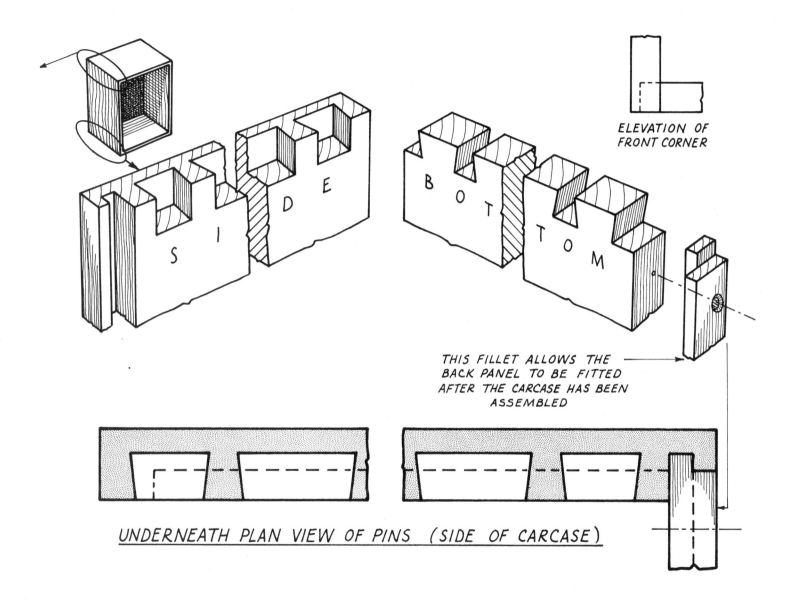

ELEVATION OF
FRONT CORNER

SIDE

BOTTOM

THIS FILLET ALLOWS THE
BACK PANEL TO BE FITTED
AFTER THE CARCASE HAS BEEN
ASSEMBLED

UNDERNEATH PLAN VIEW OF PINS (SIDE OF CARCASE)

CARCASE CONSTRUCTION—8

EXAMPLE CARCASE WITH SECRET OR DOUBLE LAPPED DOVETAILS AT THE TOP & LAP DOVETAILS AT THE BASE. MITRED AT THE TOP FRONT CORNERS, GROOVED ALL ROUND FOR PLASTIC RUNNERS & A PLANTED ON FRAMED BACK PANEL.

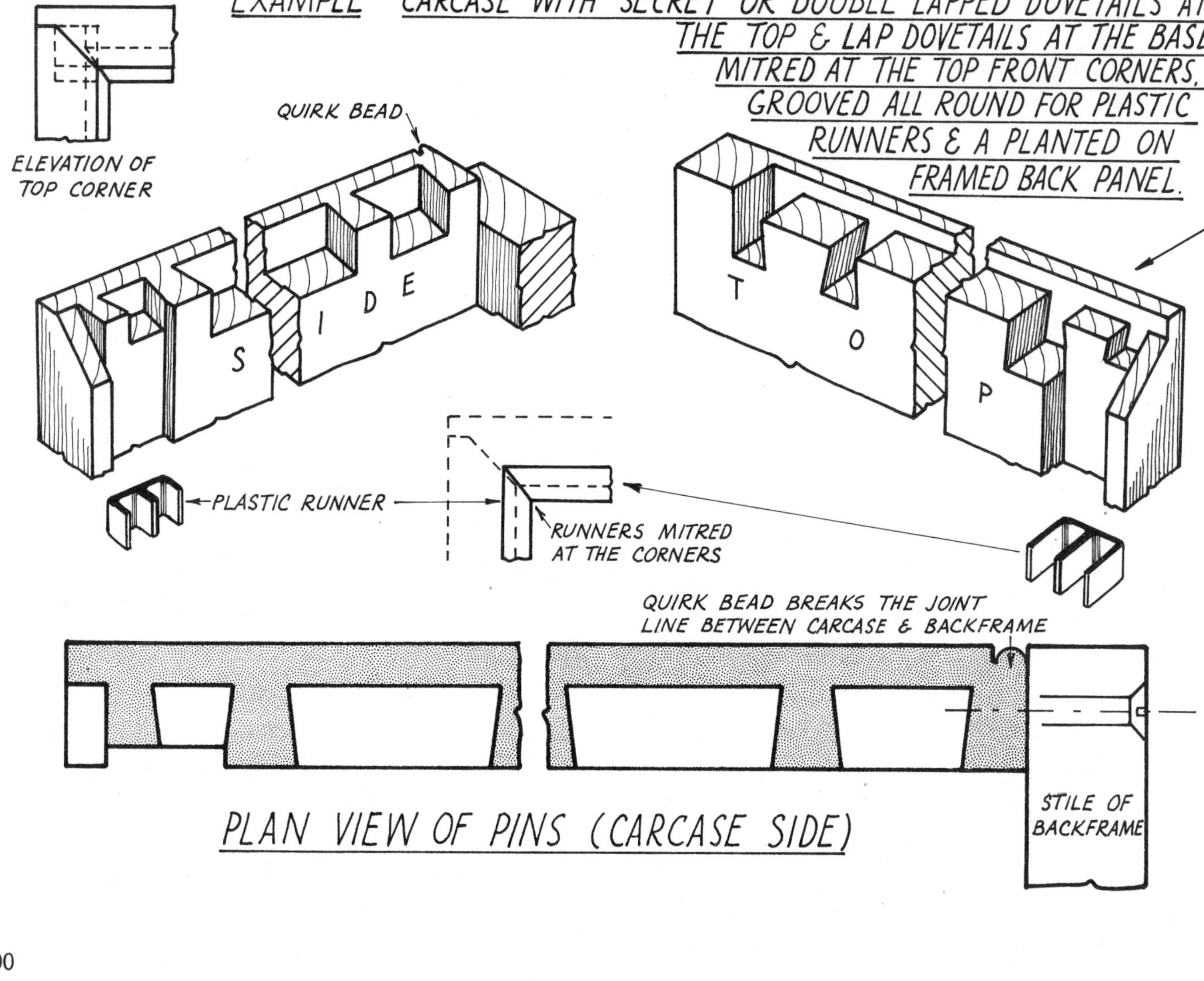

ELEVATION OF TOP CORNER

QUIRK BEAD

SIDE

TOP

PLASTIC RUNNER

RUNNERS MITRED AT THE CORNERS

QUIRK BEAD BREAKS THE JOINT LINE BETWEEN CARCASE & BACKFRAME

PLAN VIEW OF PINS (CARCASE SIDE)

STILE OF BACKFRAME

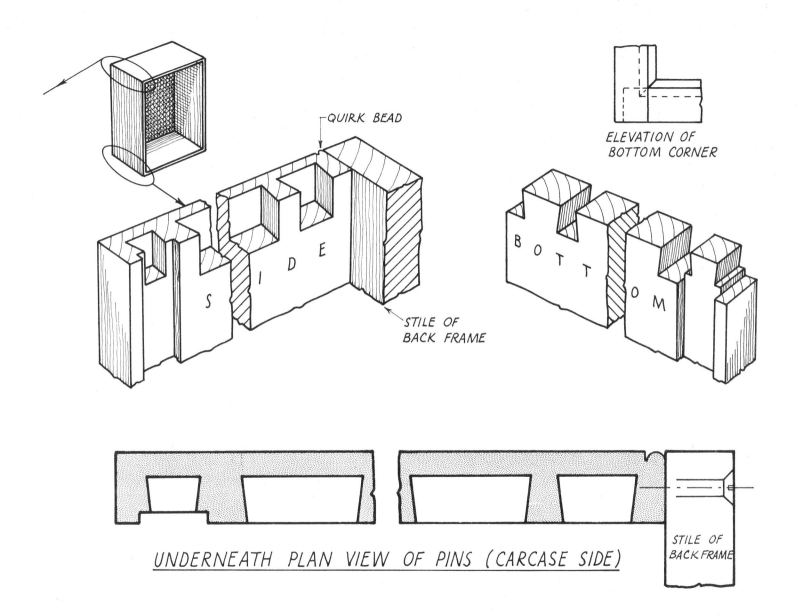

QUIRK BEAD

ELEVATION OF
BOTTOM CORNER

S I D E

STILE OF
BACK FRAME

B O T T O M

UNDERNEATH PLAN VIEW OF PINS (CARCASE SIDE)

STILE OF
BACK FRAME

EXAMPLE CARCASE WITH SECRET OR DOUBLE LAPPED DOVETAILS AT THE TOP. WIDE BEVEL ON THE FRONT EDGE – GROOVED BACK FOR PANEL – MITRED AT CORNERS

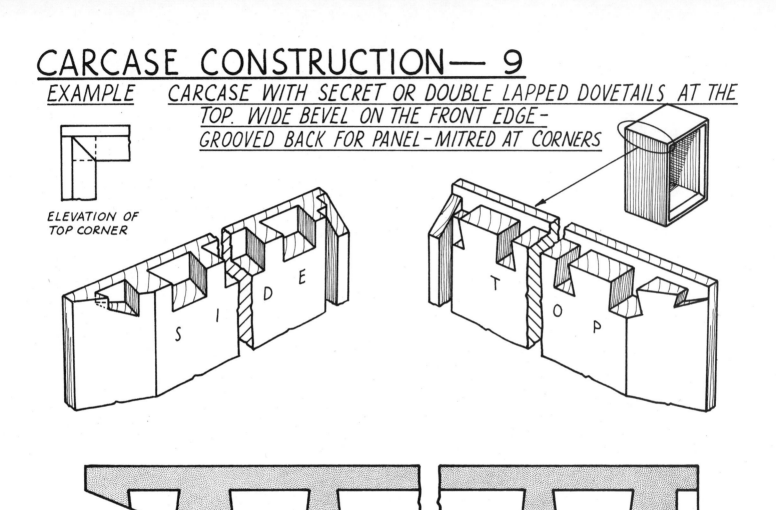

ELEVATION OF TOP CORNER

SIDE

TOP

PLAN VIEW OF PINS (CARCASE SIDE)

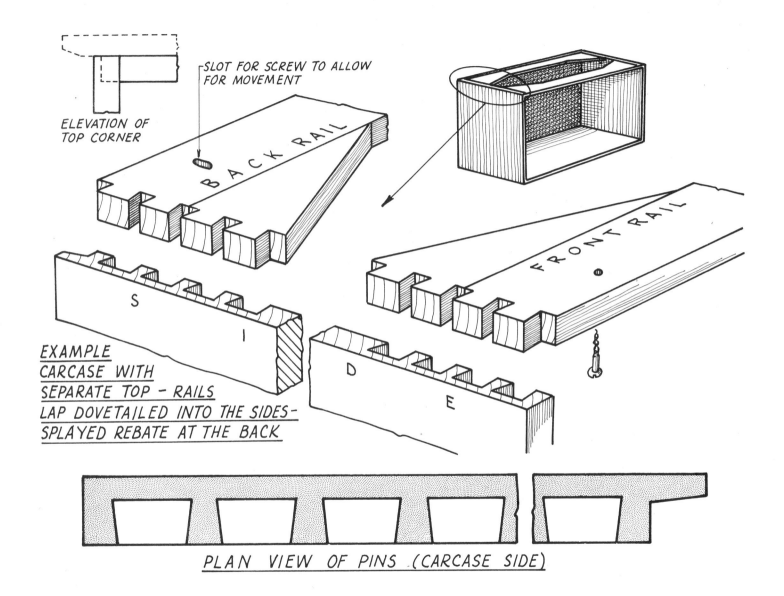

SLOT FOR SCREW TO ALLOW
FOR MOVEMENT

ELEVATION OF
TOP CORNER

B A C K   R A I L

F R O N T   R A I L

S I D E

EXAMPLE
CARCASE WITH
SEPARATE TOP – RAILS
LAP DOVETAILED INTO THE SIDES-
SPLAYED REBATE AT THE BACK

PLAN VIEW OF PINS (CARCASE SIDE)

CARCASE CONSTRUCTION—10

DIVISIONS WITHIN THE CARCASE - HORIZONTAL & VERTICAL

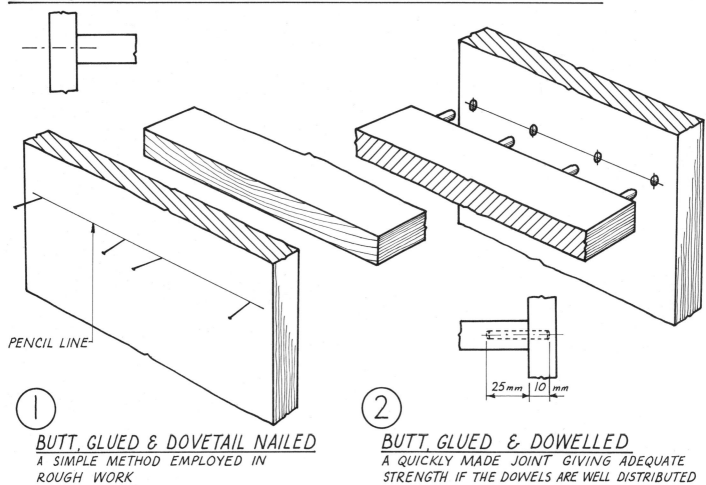

PENCIL LINE

25 mm | 10 mm

①
BUTT, GLUED & DOVETAIL NAILED
A SIMPLE METHOD EMPLOYED IN
ROUGH WORK

②
BUTT, GLUED & DOWELLED
A QUICKLY MADE JOINT GIVING ADEQUATE
STRENGTH IF THE DOWELS ARE WELL DISTRIBUTED

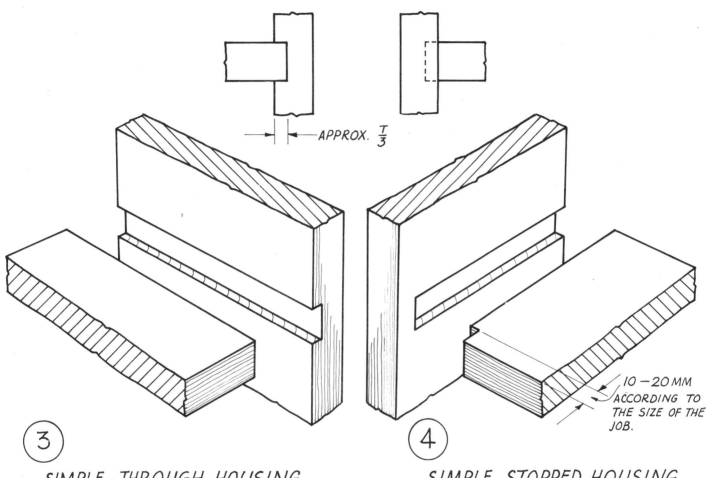

APPROX. $\frac{T}{3}$

10 — 20 MM
ACCORDING TO
THE SIZE OF THE
JOB.

③

SIMPLE THROUGH HOUSING
CAN BE GLUED AND/OR DOVETAIL NAILED.
ADEQUATE FOR ROUGH SHELVING AND BOX DIVISIONS

④

SIMPLE STOPPED HOUSING
A GLUED JOINT USED IN CABINET
MAKING

CARCASE CONSTRUCTION—11

DIVISIONS WITHIN THE CARCASE

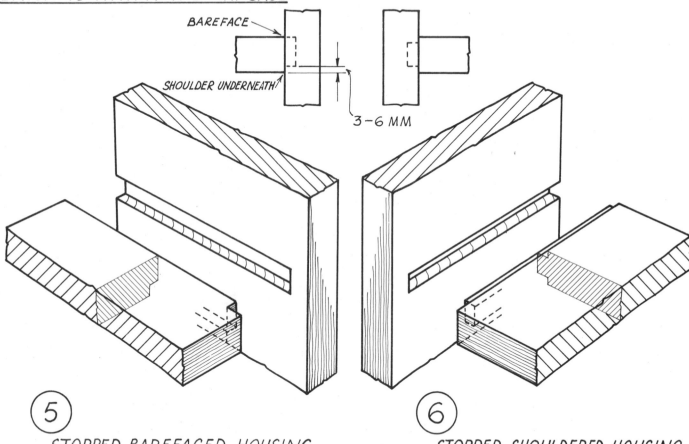

BAREFACE

SHOULDER UNDERNEATH

3–6 MM

⑤ STOPPED BAREFACED HOUSING

A CABINET MAKING JOINT. SHOULDER UNDERNEATH
PROVIDES A POSITIVE STOP WHEN ASSEMBLING

⑥ STOPPED SHOULDERED HOUSING

SIMILAR TO '5'. PARTICULARLY SUITABLE
FOR VERTICAL DIVISIONS

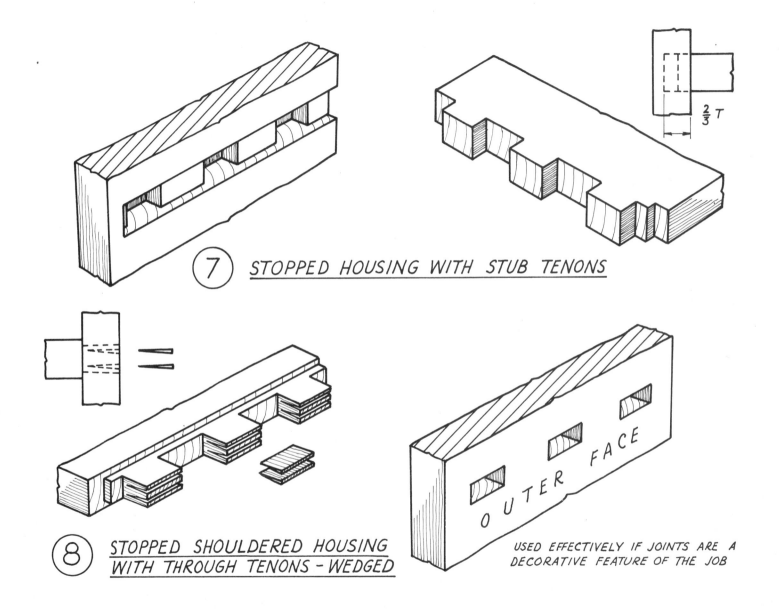

$\dfrac{2}{3} T$

⑦ STOPPED HOUSING WITH STUB TENONS

⑧ STOPPED SHOULDERED HOUSING
WITH THROUGH TENONS – WEDGED

OUTER FACE

USED EFFECTIVELY IF JOINTS ARE A
DECORATIVE FEATURE OF THE JOB

DIVISIONS WITHIN THE CARCASE

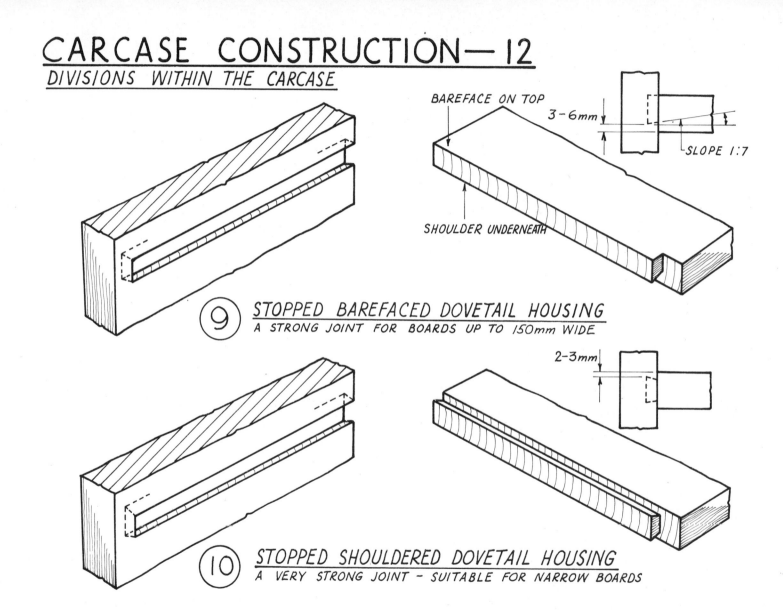

BAREFACE ON TOP

3 - 6mm

SLOPE 1:7

SHOULDER UNDERNEATH

⑨ STOPPED BAREFACED DOVETAIL HOUSING
A STRONG JOINT FOR BOARDS UP TO 150mm WIDE

2 - 3mm

⑩ STOPPED SHOULDERED DOVETAIL HOUSING
A VERY STRONG JOINT - SUITABLE FOR NARROW BOARDS

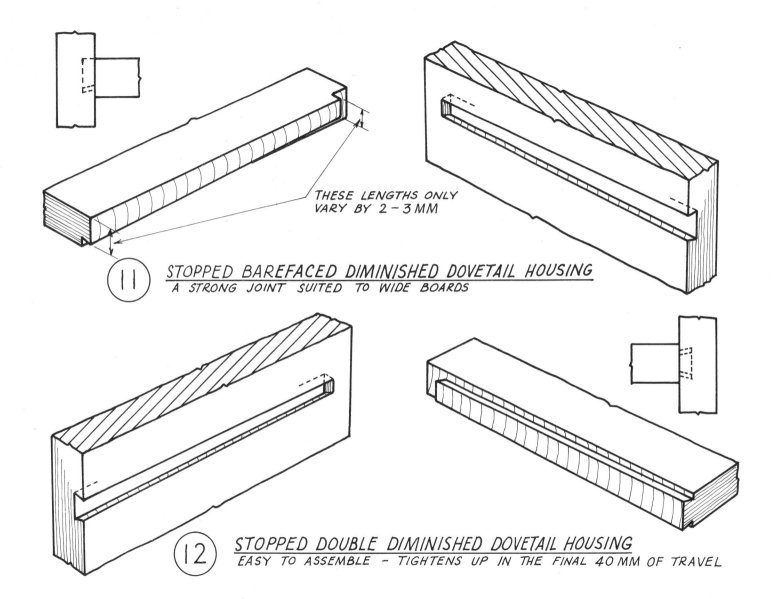

THESE LENGTHS ONLY
VARY BY 2 – 3 MM

(11) STOPPED BAREFACED DIMINISHED DOVETAIL HOUSING
A STRONG JOINT SUITED TO WIDE BOARDS

(12) STOPPED DOUBLE DIMINISHED DOVETAIL HOUSING
EASY TO ASSEMBLE – TIGHTENS UP IN THE FINAL 40 MM OF TRAVEL

CARCASE CONSTRUCTION—13

STOPPED DOUBLE DIMINISHED DOVETAIL HOUSING

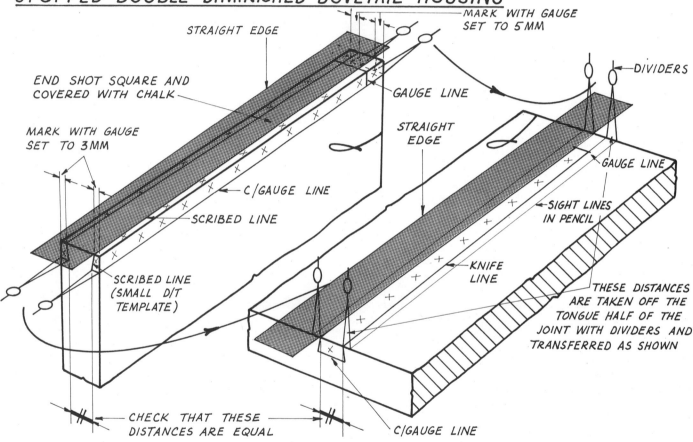

MARK WITH GAUGE SET TO 5MM

STRAIGHT EDGE

END SHOT SQUARE AND COVERED WITH CHALK

GAUGE LINE

DIVIDERS

MARK WITH GAUGE SET TO 3MM

STRAIGHT EDGE

GAUGE LINE

C/GAUGE LINE

SIGHT LINES IN PENCIL

SCRIBED LINE

SCRIBED LINE (SMALL D/T TEMPLATE)

KNIFE LINE

THESE DISTANCES ARE TAKEN OFF THE TONGUE HALF OF THE JOINT WITH DIVIDERS AND TRANSFERRED AS SHOWN

CHECK THAT THESE DISTANCES ARE EQUAL

C/GAUGE LINE

MARKING OUT DETAIL

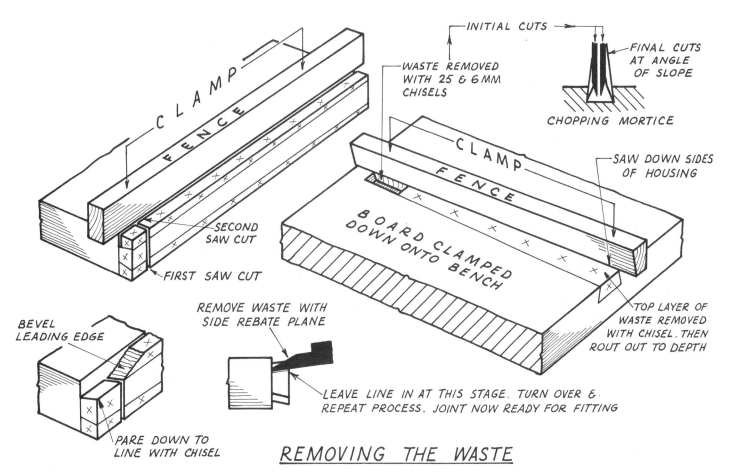

CLAMP
FENCE

INITIAL CUTS

FINAL CUTS
AT ANGLE
OF SLOPE

WASTE REMOVED
WITH 25 & 6MM
CHISELS

CHOPPING MORTICE

SECOND
SAW CUT

FIRST SAW CUT

CLAMP
FENCE

SAW DOWN SIDES
OF HOUSING

BOARD CLAMPED
DOWN ONTO BENCH

TOP LAYER OF
WASTE REMOVED
WITH CHISEL. THEN
ROUT OUT TO DEPTH

BEVEL
LEADING EDGE

REMOVE WASTE WITH
SIDE REBATE PLANE

PARE DOWN TO
LINE WITH CHISEL

LEAVE LINE IN AT THIS STAGE. TURN OVER &
REPEAT PROCESS. JOINT NOW READY FOR FITTING

REMOVING THE WASTE

FITTING THE JOINT

①CLAMP HOUSING PART OF JOINT ONTO BENCH TOP ②CHECK DEPTH OF HOUSING ③OFFER UP
TONGUE & DRIVE INTO HOUSING USING HAMMER & WASTE WOOD ④REMOVE & NOTE WHERE JOINT
SURFACES ARE RUBBING ⑤TAKE OFF HIGH SPOTS WITH SIDE REBATE PLANE ⑥CHECK FOR FIT & REPEAT
PROCESS UNTIL JOINT CAN BE DRIVEN RIGHT HOME ⑦CHECK SQUARENESS & TIGHT FIT OF SHOULDERS

CARCASE CONSTRUCTION—14

CARCASE BACKS

TYPE	MATERIAL	THICK-NESS	METHOD OF FIXING	EFFECT ON CARCASE JOINTS	USE	REMARKS
SHEET COVERING	HARDBOARD	3 OR 5 MM	1. GLUED - PINNED OR SCREWED 2. PINNED 3. SCREWED - ONTO BACK EDGE OF THE CARCASE	NIL	ROUGHER WORK - TRAYS, BOXES, KITCHEN CUP-BOARDS	SIMPLE & CHEAP
	PLYWOOD	4 TO 12 MM	AS ABOVE	NIL	AS ABOVE	THICKER PLY ADDS CONSIDERABLE STRENGTH TO A LARGE CARCASE
	HARDBOARD OR PLYWOOD	AS ABOVE	1. PINNED OR SCREWED INTO A SQUARE REBATE 2. HELD IN GROOVE	JOINT ADJUSTED TO PRODUCE A MITRED FACE OR TO FILL IN REBATE OR GROOVE	GENERAL CABINET WORK	SCREW CUPS MAY BE USED SEE DRGS NOS. 1, 2, 3, & 4
	PLY VENEERED	6 MM	REBATE OR GROOVE	AS ABOVE	DISPLAY OR SHOW CABINETS	SEE DRGS NOS. 1, 2, 3, & 4
FRAMED UP PANELS	SOLID HARDWOOD	FRAMES 16 TO 20 MM PANELS 6 TO 16 MM	1. SCREWED INTO SPLAYED REBATE 2. HELD IN GROOVE 3. PLANTED ONTO BACK EDGE OF THE CARCASE	} MUST BE ALLOWED FOR IN JOINT DESIGN NIL	HIGH CLASS HANDMADE CABINET WORK	SEE DRGS NOS. 5 & 6
MATCH BOARDING	SOFT OR HARDWOOD	12 TO 20 MM	NARROW BOARDS SCREWED INTO A SQUARE REBATE OR TONGUED INTO A GROOVE	MUST BE ALLOWED FOR IN JOINT DESIGN	OCCASIONALLY USED IN GOOD CABINET WORK	JOINT LINE BETWEEN BOARDS BROKEN WITH MOULDING RUN DOWN THE GRAIN SEE DRGS NOS. 1 TO 4 & 7 & 8

TYPES OF CARCASE BACKS & THEIR EFFECT ON CONSTRUCTION

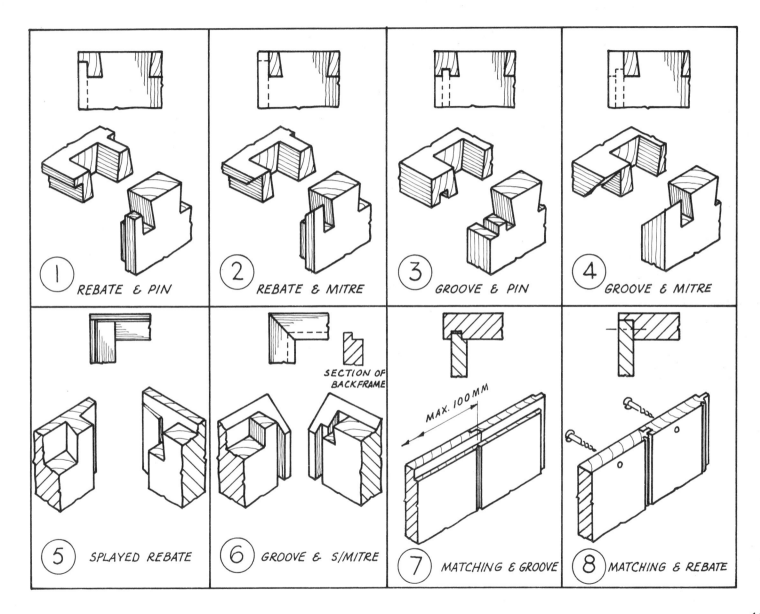

1. REBATE & PIN

2. REBATE & MITRE

3. GROOVE & PIN

4. GROOVE & MITRE

5. SPLAYED REBATE

6. GROOVE & S/MITRE

SECTION OF BACKFRAME

7. MATCHING & GROOVE

MAX. 100MM

8. MATCHING & REBATE

CARCASE CONSTRUCTION—15

REMOVABLE SHELVING

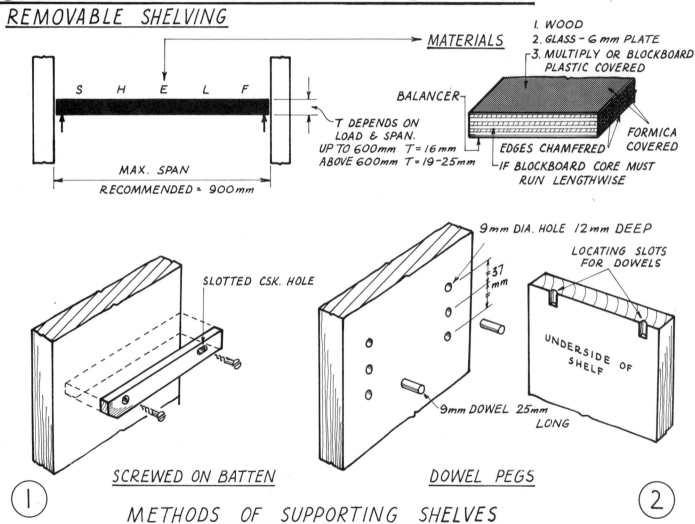

MATERIALS

1. WOOD
2. GLASS - 6 mm PLATE
3. MULTIPLY OR BLOCKBOARD
   PLASTIC COVERED

S H E L F

MAX. SPAN
RECOMMENDED = 900mm

T DEPENDS ON
LOAD & SPAN.
UP TO 600mm T=16mm
ABOVE 600mm T=19-25mm

BALANCER

FORMICA
COVERED

EDGES CHAMFERED

IF BLOCKBOARD CORE MUST
RUN LENGTHWISE

SLOTTED CSK. HOLE

SCREWED ON BATTEN

①

9mm DIA. HOLE 12mm DEEP

LOCATING SLOTS
FOR DOWELS

37 mm

9mm DOWEL 25mm LONG

UNDERSIDE OF SHELF

DOWEL PEGS

②

METHODS OF SUPPORTING SHELVES

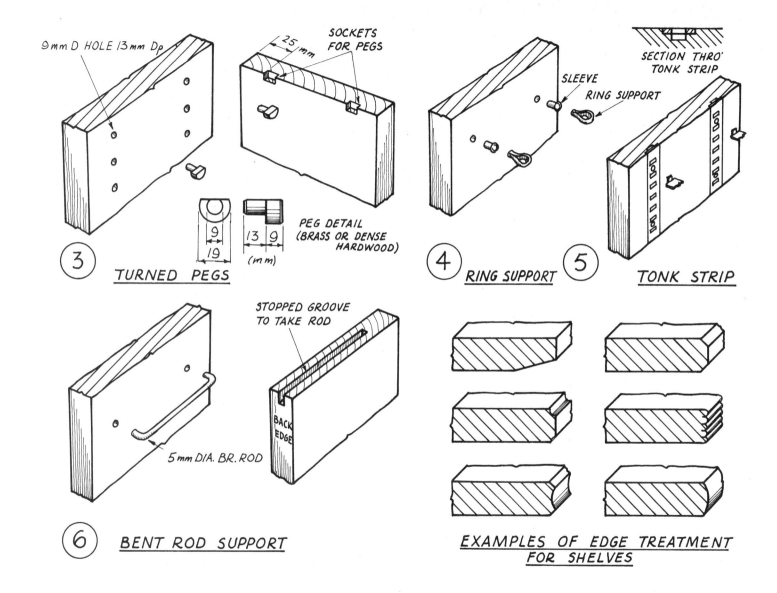

9mm D HOLE 13mm Dp

SOCKETS FOR PEGS

25 mm

③ TURNED PEGS

9
19

13 | 9

(mm)

PEG DETAIL
(BRASS OR DENSE
HARDWOOD)

SECTION THRO'
TONK STRIP

SLEEVE

RING SUPPORT

④ RING SUPPORT

⑤ TONK STRIP

STOPPED GROOVE
TO TAKE ROD

BACK
EDGE

5mm DIA. BR. ROD

⑥ BENT ROD SUPPORT

EXAMPLES OF EDGE TREATMENT
FOR SHELVES

CARCASE CONSTRUCTION—16

FRONTS—DOORS

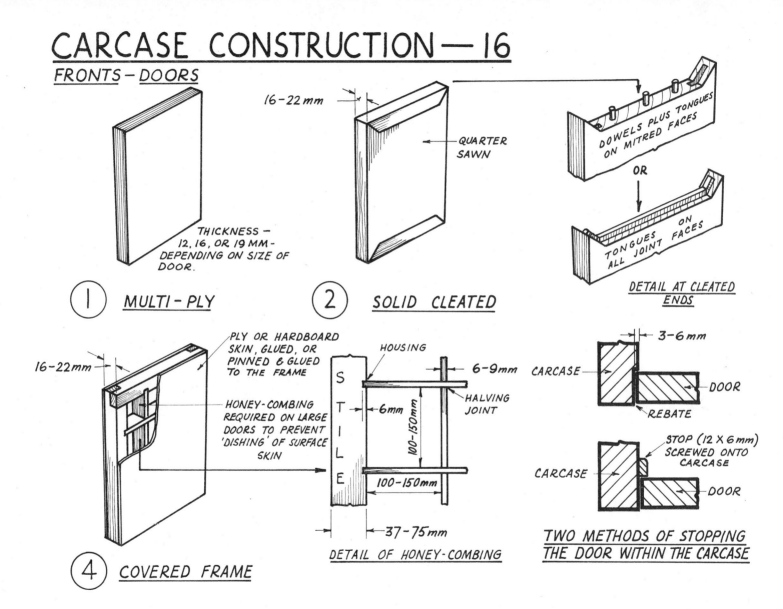

THICKNESS —
12, 16, OR 19 MM
DEPENDING ON SIZE OF
DOOR.

① MULTI-PLY

16–22 mm

QUARTER
SAWN

② SOLID CLEATED

DOWELS PLUS TONGUES
ON MITRED FACES

OR

TONGUES ON
ALL JOINT FACES

DETAIL AT CLEATED
ENDS

16–22mm

PLY OR HARDBOARD
SKIN, GLUED, OR
PINNED & GLUED
TO THE FRAME

HONEY-COMBING
REQUIRED ON LARGE
DOORS TO PREVENT
'DISHING' OF SURFACE
SKIN

④ COVERED FRAME

HOUSING

STILE

6mm

6–9mm

HALVING
JOINT

100–150mm

100–150mm

37–75mm

DETAIL OF HONEY-COMBING

3–6 mm

CARCASE

DOOR

REBATE

STOP (12 X 6mm)
SCREWED ONTO
CARCASE

CARCASE

DOOR

TWO METHODS OF STOPPING
THE DOOR WITHIN THE CARCASE

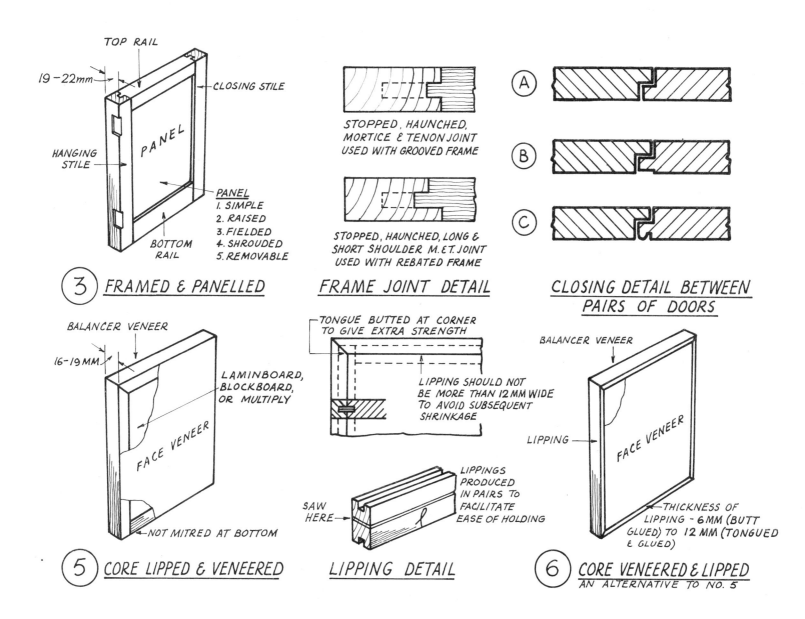

TOP RAIL

19 – 22mm

CLOSING STILE

HANGING STILE

PANEL

PANEL
1. SIMPLE
2. RAISED
3. FIELDED
4. SHROUDED
5. REMOVABLE

BOTTOM RAIL

③ FRAMED & PANELLED

STOPPED, HAUNCHED, MORTICE & TENON JOINT USED WITH GROOVED FRAME

STOPPED, HAUNCHED, LONG & SHORT SHOULDER M. & T. JOINT USED WITH REBATED FRAME

FRAME JOINT DETAIL

Ⓐ

Ⓑ

Ⓒ

CLOSING DETAIL BETWEEN PAIRS OF DOORS

BALANCER VENEER

16 – 19 MM

LAMINBOARD, BLOCKBOARD, OR MULTIPLY

FACE VENEER

NOT MITRED AT BOTTOM

⑤ CORE LIPPED & VENEERED

TONGUE BUTTED AT CORNER TO GIVE EXTRA STRENGTH

LIPPING SHOULD NOT BE MORE THAN 12 MM WIDE TO AVOID SUBSEQUENT SHRINKAGE

SAW HERE

LIPPINGS PRODUCED IN PAIRS TO FACILITATE EASE OF HOLDING

LIPPING DETAIL

BALANCER VENEER

LIPPING

FACE VENEER

THICKNESS OF LIPPING – 6 MM (BUTT GLUED) TO 12 MM (TONGUED & GLUED)

⑥ CORE VENEERED & LIPPED
AN ALTERNATIVE TO NO. 5

FRONTS   DOORS—SLIDING (WOOD)

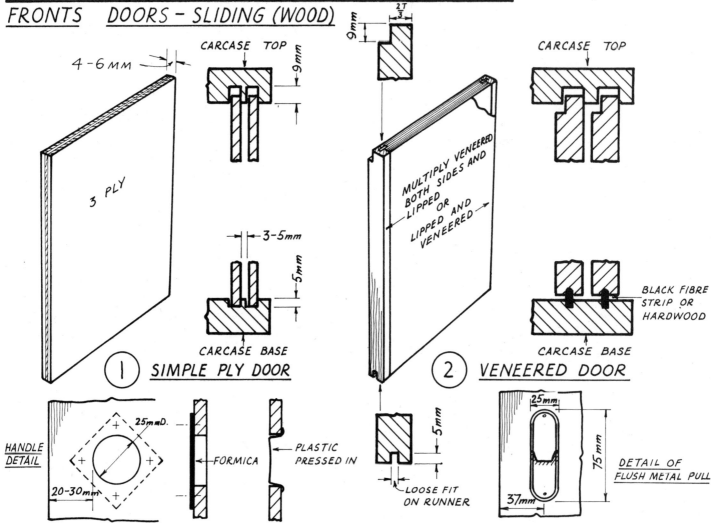

CARCASE TOP

9mm

4-6mm

3 PLY

3-5mm

5mm

CARCASE BASE

① SIMPLE PLY DOOR

HANDLE DETAIL

25mmD.

FORMICA

PLASTIC PRESSED IN

20-30mm

$\frac{2T}{3}$

9mm

CARCASE TOP

MULTIPLY VENEERED BOTH SIDES AND LIPPED OR LIPPED AND VENEERED

BLACK FIBRE STRIP OR HARDWOOD

CARCASE BASE

② VENEERED DOOR

5mm

LOOSE FIT ON RUNNER

25mm

75mm

37mm

DETAIL OF FLUSH METAL PULL

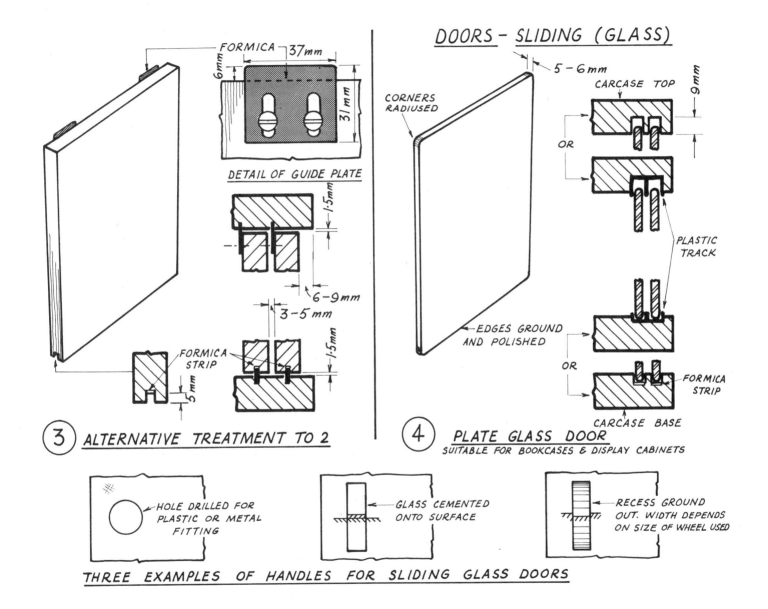

DOORS — SLIDING (GLASS)

FORMICA — 37mm

6mm

31mm

DETAIL OF GUIDE PLATE

1·5mm

6-9mm

3-5mm

1·5mm

FORMICA STRIP

5mm

(3) ALTERNATIVE TREATMENT TO 2

CORNERS RADIUSED

5 - 6mm

CARCASE TOP

9mm

OR

PLASTIC TRACK

EDGES GROUND AND POLISHED

OR

FORMICA STRIP

CARCASE BASE

(4) PLATE GLASS DOOR
SUITABLE FOR BOOKCASES & DISPLAY CABINETS

HOLE DRILLED FOR PLASTIC OR METAL FITTING

GLASS CEMENTED ONTO SURFACE

RECESS GROUND OUT. WIDTH DEPENDS ON SIZE OF WHEEL USED

THREE EXAMPLES OF HANDLES FOR SLIDING GLASS DOORS

119

CARCASE CONSTRUCTION—18

PRE-VENEERED BOARDS

VENEERED
CHIPBOARD

VENEERED CHIPBOARD
ALREADY LIPPED —
'CONTIBOARD'

MELAMINE COVERED
CHIPBOARD ALREADY
LIPPED— 'CONTIPLAS'

VENEERED
BLOCKBOARD

VENEERED
PLYWOOD

PRE-VENEERED BOARDS ARE NORMALLY SOLD
IN SHEET SIZES. THEREFORE FOR THE SAKE
OF ECONOMY THE SIZE OF A JOB SHOULD BE
RELATED TO THESE BOARDS IF POSSIBLE.

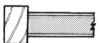 ← SURPLUS REMOVED

THE LIPPING SHOULD BE ABOUT 2 MM
THICKER THAN THE BOARD TO ALLOW
FOR TOLERANCE WHEN GLUING IT IN
POSITION
THE SURPLUS CAN BE PLANED DOWN
AFTERWARDS

EDGE TREATMENTS

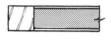
PANELS NEED TO BE LIPPED WITH THE
SAME WOOD AS THE VENEER UNLESS A
CONTRASTING EDGE IS REQUIRED

THESE BOARDS ARE BOUGHT IN MODULAR
SIZES. WHEN THEY ARE CUT THE RAW
EDGES MAY BE COVERED WITH SELF
ADHESIVE STRIP APPLIED WITH A HOT
IRON AND BROWN PAPER

AS ABOVE

NEEDS TO BE LIPPED WITH A MATCHING
OR CONTRASTING TIMBER

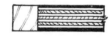
AS ABOVE

PLYWOOD LIPPED FIRST AND
THEN VENEERED

ONE METHOD
OF JOINING
TWO LIPPED
BOARDS AT
RT ANGLES
USING DOWELS
AND GLUE

 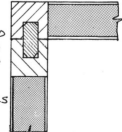

CORNER JOINTS USING MANUFACTURED BOARDS

①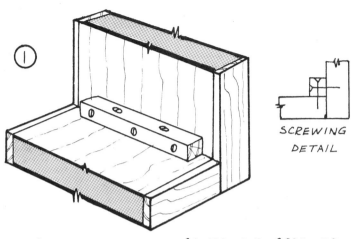

SCREWING
DETAIL

SQUARE BATTEN GLUED AND SCREWED

②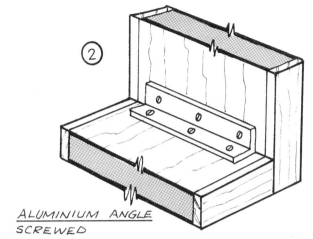

ALUMINIUM ANGLE
SCREWED
A STRONGER FIXING MAY BE OBTAINED IF
'ARALDITE' GLUE IS USED AS WELL AS SCREWS

③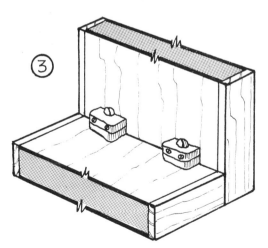

NYLON FITTING DESIGNED FOR KNOCK
DOWN FURNITURE PLACE AT 150-
200mm CENTRES

④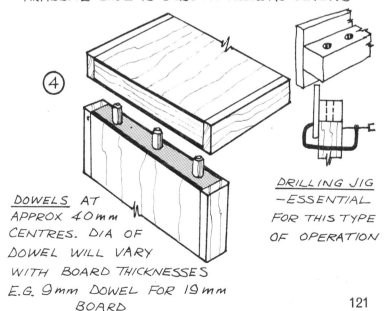

DRILLING JIG
—ESSENTIAL
FOR THIS TYPE
OF OPERATION

DOWELS AT
APPROX 40mm
CENTRES. DIA OF
DOWEL WILL VARY
WITH BOARD THICKNESSES
E.G. 9mm DOWEL FOR 19mm
BOARD

PRE-VENEERED FURNITURE

TEAK VENEER

HANDLE DETAIL

AL. ANGLE SET
ABOVE THE CENTRE
HEIGHT OF CARCASE

RECORD CABINET — DESIGNED AND MADE BY BARRY PAYNE

CONSTRUCTION

CARCASE — PRE-VENEERED 12 MM PLY PANELS
CARCASE JOINTS — DOWELS AT 40 MM CENTRES
DOORS — 12 MM PLY LIPPED & VENEERED
STOOL -- RAILS — PLY VENEERED OR SOLID
TEAK
LEGS — 25 MM SQUARE ALUMINIUM
TUBING

AL. STRIP SET VERTICALLY
IN THE CARCASE TO ACT
AS A LINK WITH THE
METAL LEGS OF THE STOOL

LEG DETAIL

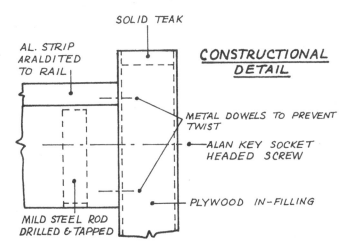

SOLID TEAK

AL. STRIP ARALDITED TO RAIL

CONSTRUCTIONAL DETAIL

METAL DOWELS TO PREVENT TWIST

ALAN KEY SOCKET HEADED SCREW

PLYWOOD IN-FILLING

MILD STEEL ROD DRILLED & TAPPED

COFFEE TABLE — DESIGNED AND MADE BY STEWART MOTHERSHAW

CONSTRUCTION

TOP — 12 MM PLY LIPPED AND VENEERED IN TEAK ON BOTH FACES.

RAILS — PLY VENEERED ON FACES AND EDGES OR SOLID TEAK.

LEGS — 25 MM SQUARE ALUMINIUM TUBING

SHELF — 6 MM PLATE GLASS.

NOTE HOW THE AL. STRIP HAS BEEN USED TO LINK THE FOUR LEGS TOGETHER AND THE SPECIAL TREATMENT OF THE TOP AROUND THEM.

LEG DETAIL

DRAWERS—1

① SOLID DRAWER FRONTS FRAMED UP/SOLID DIVISIONS

② VENEERED DRAWER FRONTS SET BACK DIVISIONS

③ VENEERED DRAWER FRONTS RETURNED ROUND CARCASE SIDES

NOTE. 1. VARIATION IN DRAWER DEPTHS 2. HANDLES ABOVE CENTRE 3. HANDLES A 'COMFORTABLE' DISTANCE APART

THE INFLUENCE OF DRAWER TREATMENT ON DESIGN

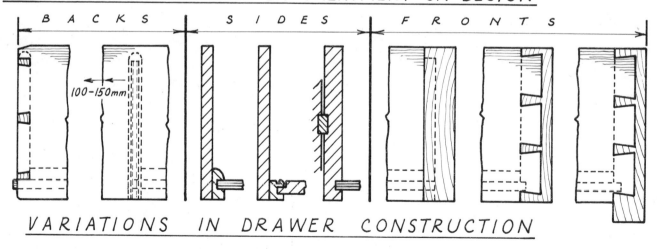

BACKS   SIDES   FRONTS

100-150mm

VARIATIONS IN DRAWER CONSTRUCTION

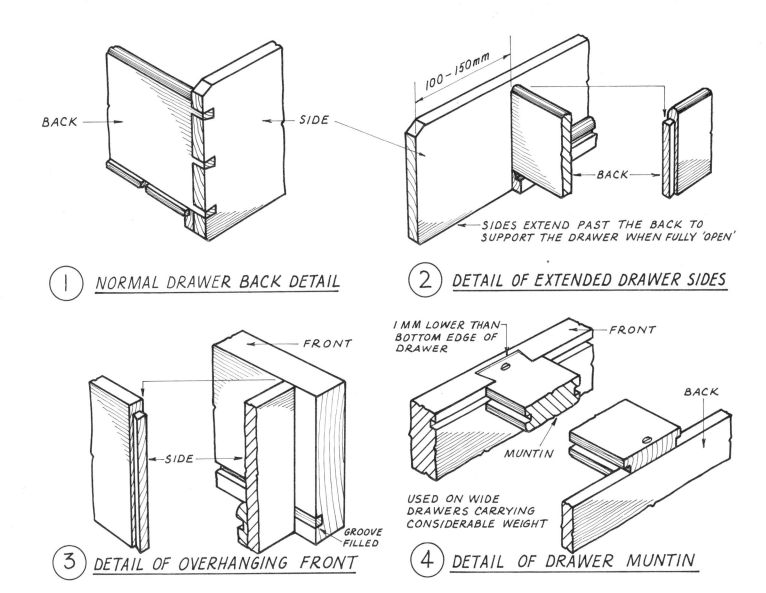

BACK ← → SIDE

① NORMAL DRAWER BACK DETAIL

100 – 150mm

← BACK →

SIDES EXTEND PAST THE BACK TO
SUPPORT THE DRAWER WHEN FULLY 'OPEN'

② DETAIL OF EXTENDED DRAWER SIDES

FRONT

← SIDE

GROOVE
FILLED

③ DETAIL OF OVERHANGING FRONT

1 MM LOWER THAN
BOTTOM EDGE OF
DRAWER

FRONT

BACK

MUNTIN

USED ON WIDE
DRAWERS CARRYING
CONSIDERABLE WEIGHT

④ DETAIL OF DRAWER MUNTIN

DRAWERS — 2
SIMPLE CONSTRUCTION

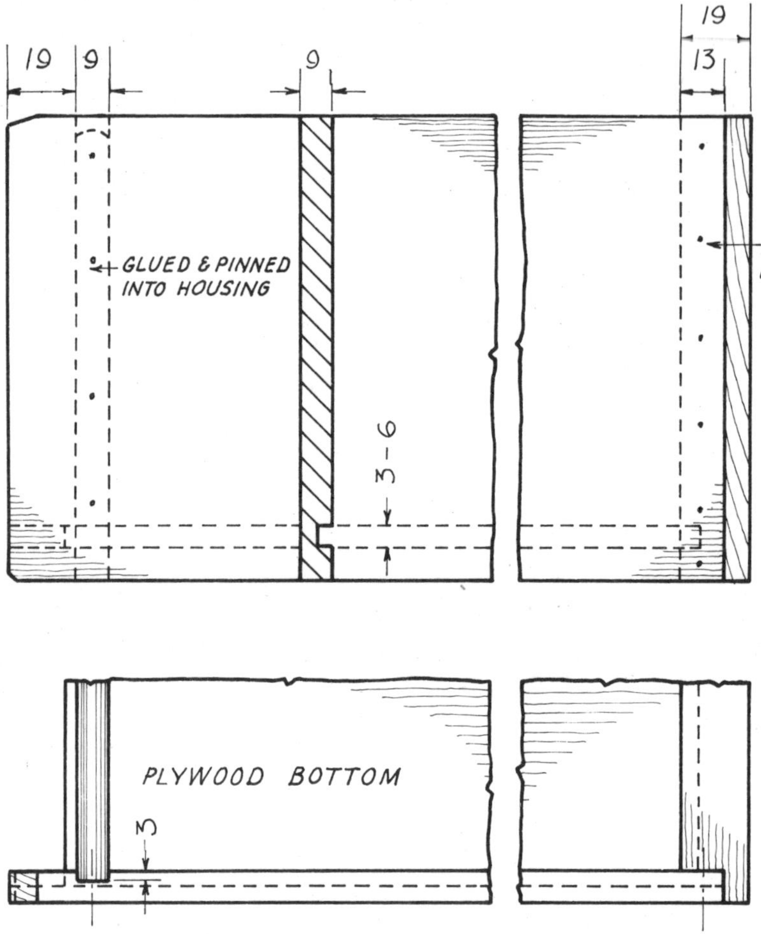

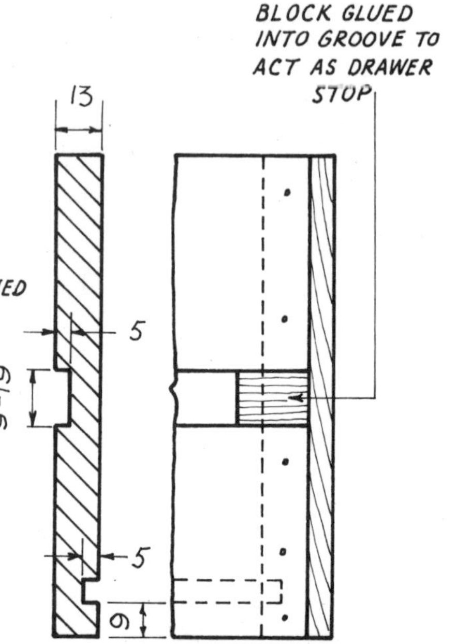

19 9   9

19
13

BLOCK GLUED
INTO GROOVE TO
ACT AS DRAWER
STOP

13

←GLUED & PINNED
INTO HOUSING

GLUED & PINNED
INTO REBATE

5

9-19

3-6

5

9

**ALTERNATIVE METHOD — DRAWER IS
SUSPENDED ON HARDWOOD FILLETS**

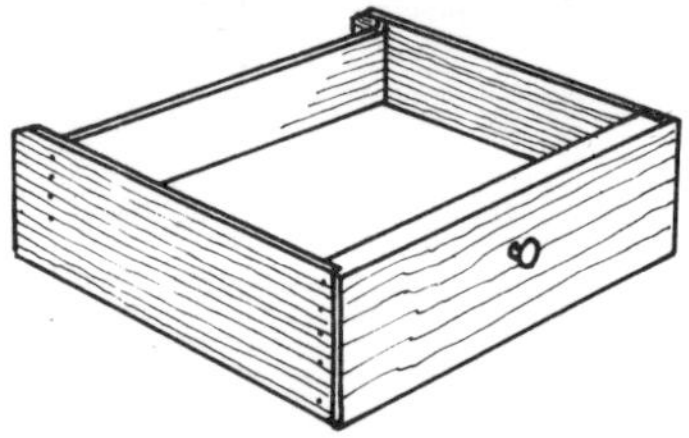

PLYWOOD BOTTOM

3

PICTORIAL VIEW OF DRAWER

DETAILS OF A DRAWER SUITABLE FOR USE IN A KITCHEN FITMENT
ALL MEASUREMENTS ARE IN MMs

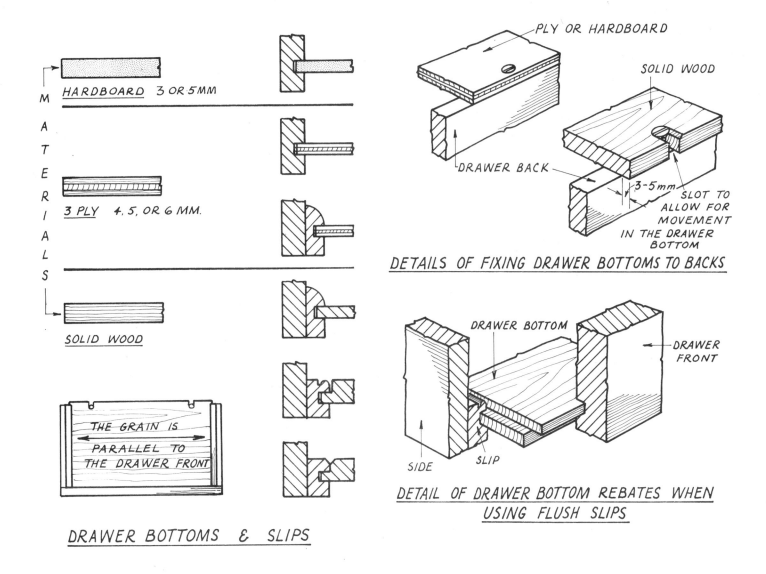

M
A
T
E
R
I
A
L
S

HARDBOARD 3 OR 5MM

3 PLY 4, 5, OR 6 MM.

SOLID WOOD

THE GRAIN IS PARALLEL TO THE DRAWER FRONT

DRAWER BOTTOMS & SLIPS

PLY OR HARDBOARD

SOLID WOOD

DRAWER BACK

3-5mm

SLOT TO ALLOW FOR MOVEMENT IN THE DRAWER BOTTOM

DETAILS OF FIXING DRAWER BOTTOMS TO BACKS

DRAWER BOTTOM

DRAWER FRONT

SIDE

SLIP

DETAIL OF DRAWER BOTTOM REBATES WHEN USING FLUSH SLIPS

DRAWERS—3
CARCASE REQUIREMENTS

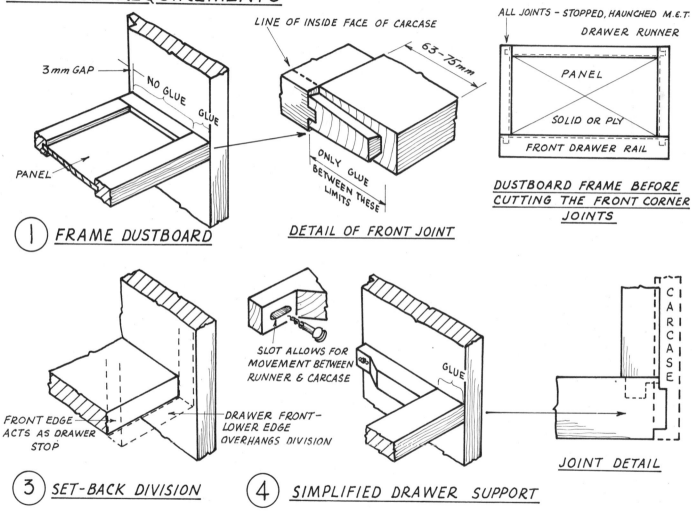

3mm GAP

NO GLUE

GLUE

PANEL

① **FRAME DUSTBOARD**

LINE OF INSIDE FACE OF CARCASE

63 – 75mm

ONLY GLUE BETWEEN THESE LIMITS

DETAIL OF FRONT JOINT

ALL JOINTS - STOPPED, HAUNCHED M.E.T.

DRAWER RUNNER

PANEL

SOLID OR PLY

FRONT DRAWER RAIL

DUSTBOARD FRAME BEFORE CUTTING THE FRONT CORNER JOINTS

FRONT EDGE ACTS AS DRAWER STOP

DRAWER FRONT - LOWER EDGE OVERHANGS DIVISION

③ **SET-BACK DIVISION**

SLOT ALLOWS FOR MOVEMENT BETWEEN RUNNER & CARCASE

GLUE

CARCASE

JOINT DETAIL

④ **SIMPLIFIED DRAWER SUPPORT**

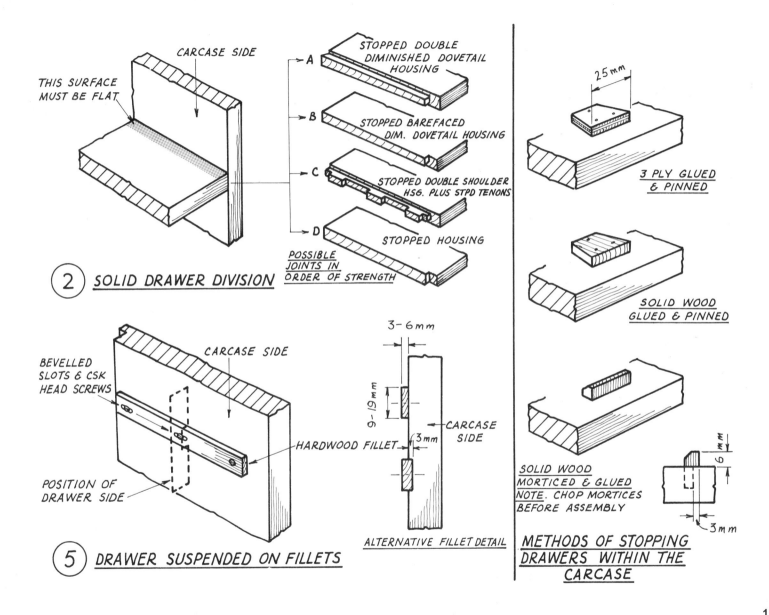

CARCASE SIDE

THIS SURFACE MUST BE FLAT

A — STOPPED DOUBLE DIMINISHED DOVETAIL HOUSING

B — STOPPED BAREFACED DIM. DOVETAIL HOUSING

C — STOPPED DOUBLE SHOULDER HSG. PLUS STPD TENONS

D — STOPPED HOUSING

POSSIBLE JOINTS IN ORDER OF STRENGTH

2 SOLID DRAWER DIVISION

25 mm

3 PLY GLUED & PINNED

SOLID WOOD GLUED & PINNED

BEVELLED SLOTS & CSK HEAD SCREWS

CARCASE SIDE

HARDWOOD FILLET

POSITION OF DRAWER SIDE

5 DRAWER SUSPENDED ON FILLETS

3 – 6 mm

9 – 19 mm

3 mm

CARCASE SIDE

ALTERNATIVE FILLET DETAIL

SOLID WOOD MORTICED & GLUED NOTE. CHOP MORTICES BEFORE ASSEMBLY

6 mm

6

3 mm

METHODS OF STOPPING DRAWERS WITHIN THE CARCASE

129

STOOL CONSTRUCTION—1
SUPPORTS FOR CARCASES

① SIMPLE FORM

② LONG STOOLS REQUIRE INTERMEDIATE STRETCHERS

③

④ FRONT RAIL SET BACK — UNSEEN FROM NORMAL VIEWPOINT

⑤

⑥ TALL STOOLS REQUIRE EXTRA MEMBERS FOR ADDITIONAL SUPPORT

⑦

⑧

⑨ STOOL WITH LOWER SHELF

IT IS DIFFICULT TO DETERMINE THE EXACT FORM AND DIMENSIONS OF A STOOL FOR A CARCASE UNTIL THE LATTER HAS BEEN MADE. THE CARCASE CAN THEN BE SUPPORTED AT A SUITABLE HEIGHT AND THE FINAL FORM OF THE STOOL ARRIVED AT BY OFFERING UP SECTIONS OF MATERIAL IN SUITABLE POSITIONS RELATIVE ONE TO THE OTHER.
NOTE. SUITABLE JOINT FORMS ARE SHOWN ON PAGES 132—134

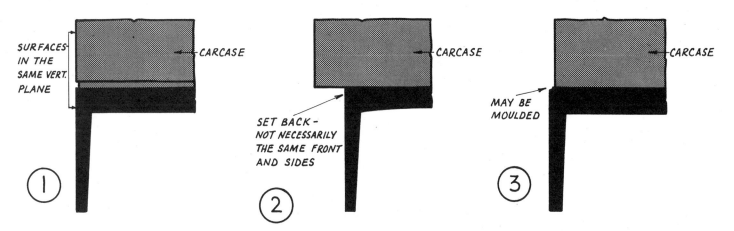

SURFACES IN THE SAME VERT. PLANE — CARCASE ①

SET BACK — NOT NECESSARILY THE SAME FRONT AND SIDES — CARCASE ②

MAY BE MOULDED — CARCASE ③

POSSIBLE POSITIONS OF THE STOOL RELATIVE TO THE CARCASE

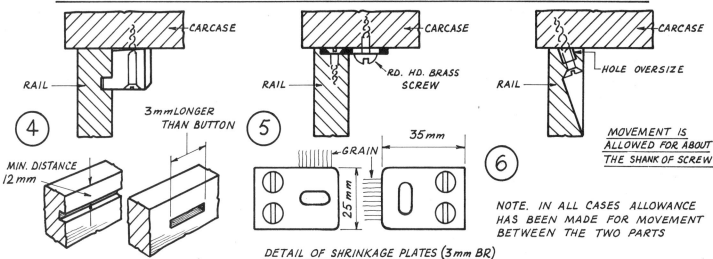

④ CARCASE — RAIL
3 mm LONGER THAN BUTTON
MIN. DISTANCE 12 mm
BUTTON HELD IN GROOVE/MORTICE

⑤ CARCASE — RD. HD. BRASS SCREW — RAIL
— GRAIN — 35 mm — 25 mm
DETAIL OF SHRINKAGE PLATES (3 mm BR)

⑥ CARCASE — HOLE OVERSIZE — RAIL
MOVEMENT IS ALLOWED FOR ABOUT THE SHANK OF SCREW

NOTE. IN ALL CASES ALLOWANCE HAS BEEN MADE FOR MOVEMENT BETWEEN THE TWO PARTS

METHODS OF FIXING THE STOOL TO THE CARCASE

STOOL CONSTRUCTION— 2
JOINTS BETWEEN LEGS AND RAILS

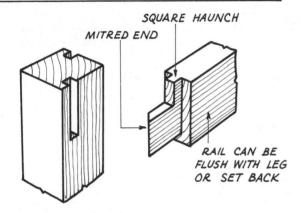

SQUARE HAUNCH

MITRED END

RAIL CAN BE FLUSH WITH LEG OR SET BACK

① STOPPED, HAUNCHED, MORTICE & TENON

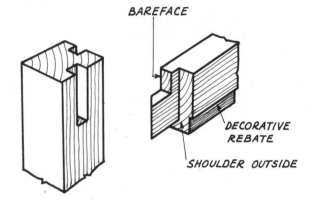

BAREFACE

DECORATIVE REBATE

SHOULDER OUTSIDE

② STOPPED, HAUNCHED, BAREFACED, M. & T.

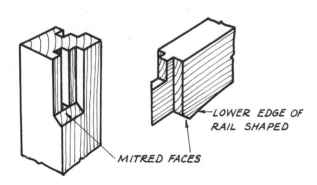

LOWER EDGE OF RAIL SHAPED

MITRED FACES

③ M. & T. WITH RAIL SET INTO THE LEG

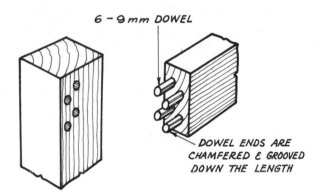

6 – 9 mm DOWEL

DOWEL ENDS ARE CHAMFERED & GROOVED DOWN THE LENGTH

④ SIMPLE DOWELLED JOINT

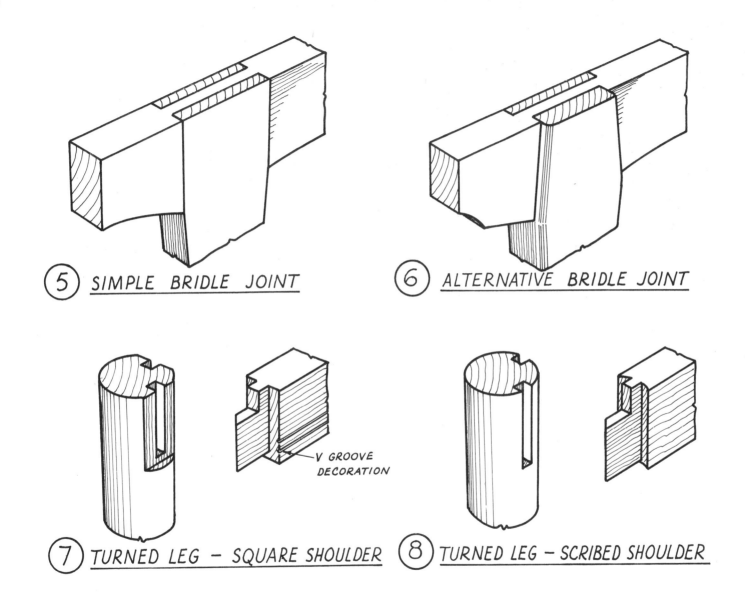

⑤ SIMPLE BRIDLE JOINT

⑥ ALTERNATIVE BRIDLE JOINT

V GROOVE
DECORATION

⑦ TURNED LEG — SQUARE SHOULDER

⑧ TURNED LEG — SCRIBED SHOULDER

STOOL CONSTRUCTION — 3

JOINTS BETWEEN RAILS AND STRETCHERS

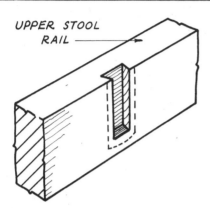

UPPER STOOL RAIL

STRETCHER

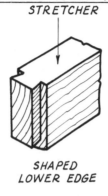

SHAPED LOWER EDGE

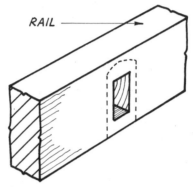

RAIL

STRETCHER

(1) STOPPED DOVETAIL HOUSING

(2) STOPPED OR THROUGH M. & T.

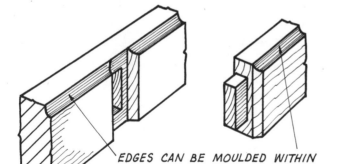

EDGES CAN BE MOULDED WITHIN THE LIMITS OF THE MITRED FACES

(3) STOPPED M. & T. WITH MITRED SHOULDERS

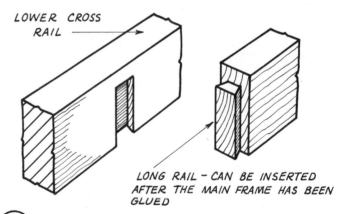

LOWER CROSS RAIL

LONG RAIL — CAN BE INSERTED AFTER THE MAIN FRAME HAS BEEN GLUED

(4) STOPPED D/T. HSG. FLUSH ON THE EDGES

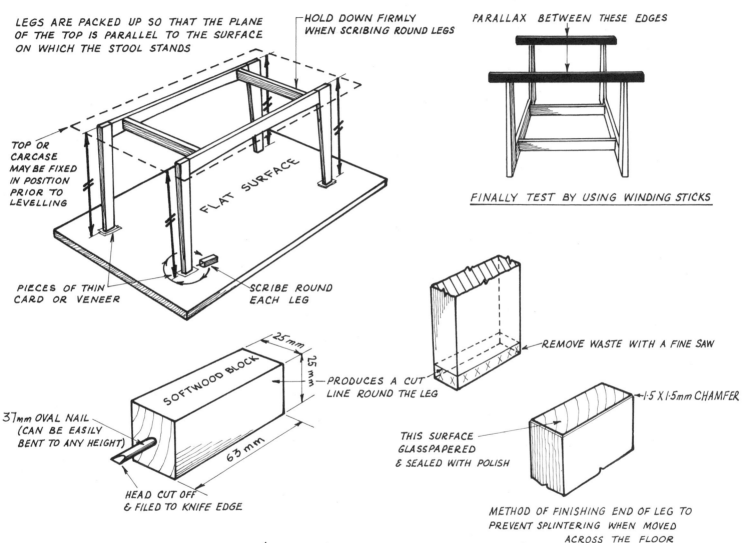

LEGS ARE PACKED UP SO THAT THE PLANE OF THE TOP IS PARALLEL TO THE SURFACE ON WHICH THE STOOL STANDS

HOLD DOWN FIRMLY WHEN SCRIBING ROUND LEGS

PARALLAX BETWEEN THESE EDGES

TOP OR CARCASE MAY BE FIXED IN POSITION PRIOR TO LEVELLING

FLAT SURFACE

FINALLY TEST BY USING WINDING STICKS

PIECES OF THIN CARD OR VENEER

SCRIBE ROUND EACH LEG

25 mm

25 mm

SOFTWOOD BLOCK

REMOVE WASTE WITH A FINE SAW

PRODUCES A CUT LINE ROUND THE LEG

37mm OVAL NAIL (CAN BE EASILY BENT TO ANY HEIGHT)

63 mm

1·5 X 1·5mm CHAMFER

THIS SURFACE GLASSPAPERED & SEALED WITH POLISH

HEAD CUT OFF & FILED TO KNIFE EDGE.

METHOD OF FINISHING END OF LEG TO PREVENT SPLINTERING WHEN MOVED ACROSS THE FLOOR

LEVELLING STOOL/TABLE CONSTRUCTIONS

STOOL CONSTRUCTION—4

CONSTRUCTIONS USING WOOD AND METAL

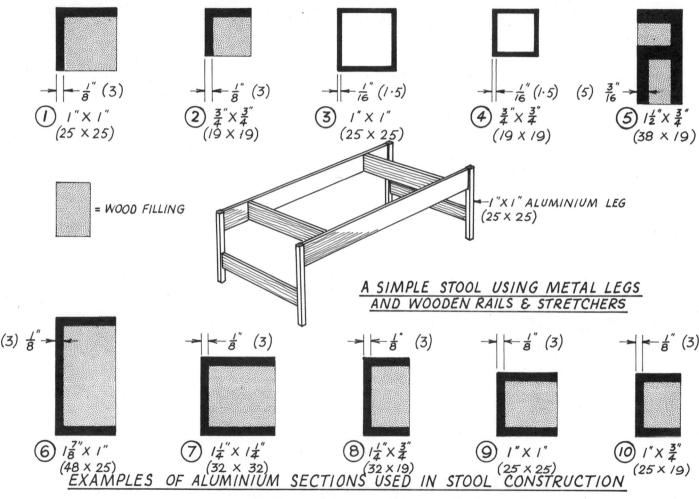

$\frac{1}{8}$" (3)

① 1"×1" (25 × 25)

② $\frac{3}{4}$"×$\frac{3}{4}$" (19 × 19)

$\frac{1}{8}$" (3)

③ 1"×1" (25 × 25)

$\frac{1}{16}$" (1·5)

④ $\frac{3}{4}$"×$\frac{3}{4}$" (19 × 19)

$\frac{1}{16}$" (1·5)

(5) $\frac{3}{16}$"

⑤ 1$\frac{1}{2}$"×$\frac{3}{4}$" (38 × 19)

= WOOD FILLING

1"×1" ALUMINIUM LEG (25 × 25)

A SIMPLE STOOL USING METAL LEGS AND WOODEN RAILS & STRETCHERS

(3) $\frac{1}{8}$"

⑥ 1$\frac{7}{8}$"×1" (48 × 25)

$\frac{1}{8}$" (3)

⑦ 1$\frac{1}{4}$"×1$\frac{1}{4}$" (32 × 32)

$\frac{1}{8}$" (3)

⑧ 1$\frac{1}{4}$"×$\frac{3}{4}$" (32 × 19)

$\frac{1}{8}$" (3)

⑨ 1"×1" (25 × 25)

$\frac{1}{8}$" (3)

⑩ 1"×$\frac{3}{4}$" (25 × 19)

EXAMPLES OF ALUMINIUM SECTIONS USED IN STOOL CONSTRUCTION

FIGURES IN ( ) INDICATE MM EQUIVALENTS

METHODS OF JOINTING SQ. AL. TUBING TO WOODEN RAILS

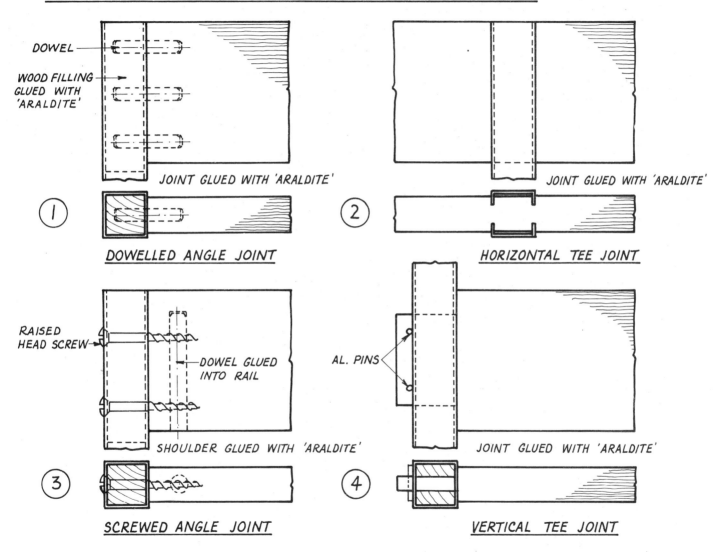

DOWEL

WOOD FILLING GLUED WITH 'ARALDITE'

JOINT GLUED WITH 'ARALDITE'

① DOWELLED ANGLE JOINT

JOINT GLUED WITH 'ARALDITE'

② HORIZONTAL TEE JOINT

RAISED HEAD SCREW

DOWEL GLUED INTO RAIL

SHOULDER GLUED WITH 'ARALDITE'

③ SCREWED ANGLE JOINT

AL. PINS

JOINT GLUED WITH 'ARALDITE'

④ VERTICAL TEE JOINT

PLINTH CONSTRUCTION

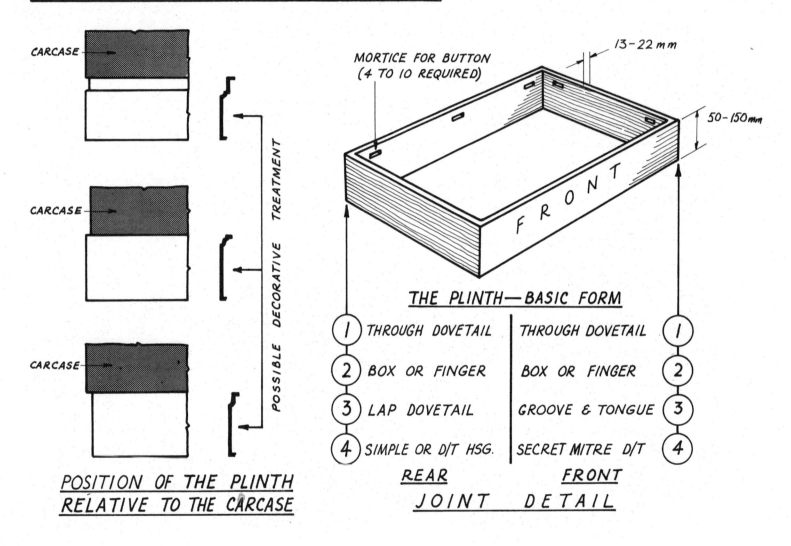

CARCASE

CARCASE

CARCASE

POSSIBLE DECORATIVE TREATMENT

POSITION OF THE PLINTH RELATIVE TO THE CARCASE

MORTICE FOR BUTTON
(4 TO 10 REQUIRED)

13–22 mm

50–150 mm

F R O N T

THE PLINTH—BASIC FORM

	REAR	FRONT	
①	THROUGH DOVETAIL	THROUGH DOVETAIL	①
②	BOX OR FINGER	BOX OR FINGER	②
③	LAP DOVETAIL	GROOVE & TONGUE	③
④	SIMPLE OR D/T HSG.	SECRET MITRE D/T	④

JOINT DETAIL

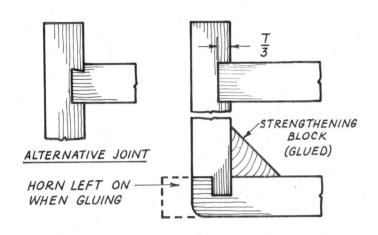

ALTERNATIVE JOINT

HORN LEFT ON WHEN GLUING

$\frac{T}{3}$

STRENGTHENING BLOCK (GLUED)

SIMPLE FORM OF CONSTRUCTION

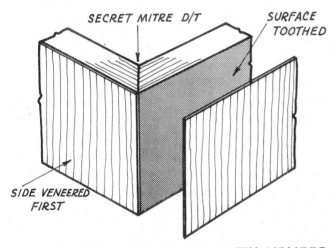

SECRET MITRE D/T

SURFACE TOOTHED

SIDE VENEERED FIRST

PLINTH CROSS BANDED WITH VENEER

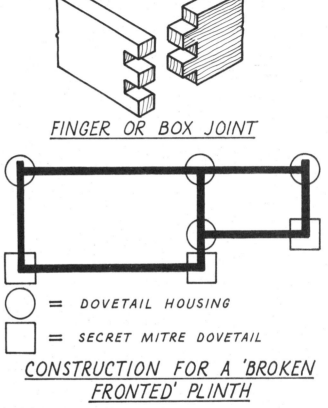

FINGER OR BOX JOINT

◯ = DOVETAIL HOUSING

☐ = SECRET MITRE DOVETAIL

CONSTRUCTION FOR A 'BROKEN FRONTED' PLINTH

1. BUTTONS
2. SHRINKAGE PLATES
3. POCKET SCREWS

METHODS OF FIXING PLINTH TO CARCASE

TABLE CONSTRUCTION — 1

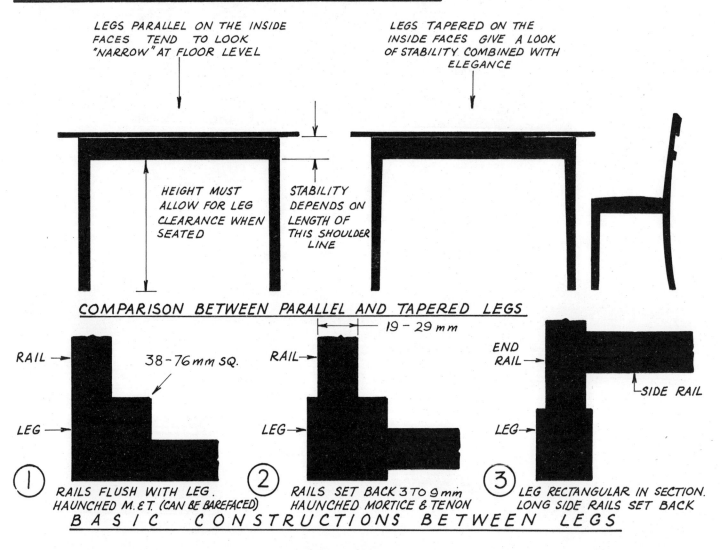

LEGS PARALLEL ON THE INSIDE FACES TEND TO LOOK "NARROW" AT FLOOR LEVEL

LEGS TAPERED ON THE INSIDE FACES GIVE A LOOK OF STABILITY COMBINED WITH ELEGANCE

HEIGHT MUST ALLOW FOR LEG CLEARANCE WHEN SEATED

STABILITY DEPENDS ON LENGTH OF THIS SHOULDER LINE

COMPARISON BETWEEN PARALLEL AND TAPERED LEGS

RAIL

38-76 mm SQ.

LEG

① RAILS FLUSH WITH LEG. HAUNCHED M.&T. (CAN BE BAREFACED)

19 - 29 mm

RAIL →

LEG →

② RAILS SET BACK 3 TO 9 mm HAUNCHED MORTICE & TENON

END RAIL

SIDE RAIL

LEG →

③ LEG RECTANGULAR IN SECTION. LONG SIDE RAILS SET BACK

BASIC CONSTRUCTIONS BETWEEN LEGS

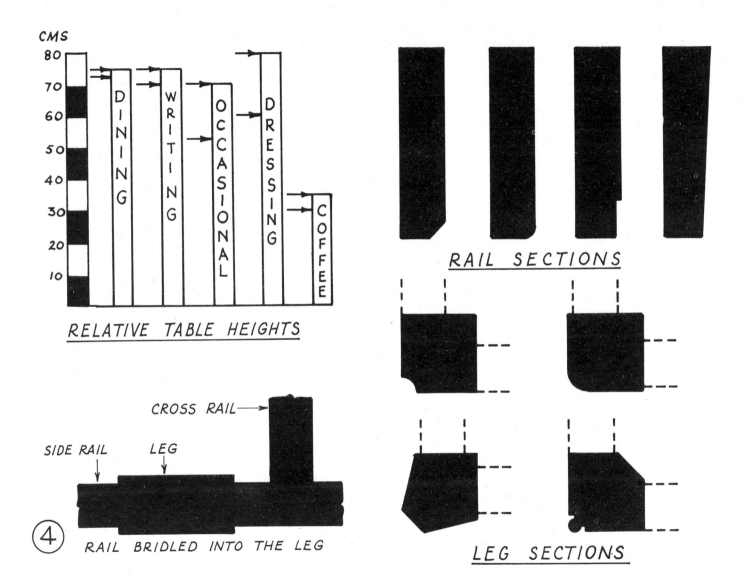

RELATIVE TABLE HEIGHTS

RAIL SECTIONS

④ RAIL BRIDLED INTO THE LEG

CROSS RAIL

SIDE RAIL   LEG

LEG SECTIONS

CMS
80
70
60
50
40
30
20
10

DINING WRITING OCCASIONAL DRESSING COFFEE

TABLE CONSTRUCTION — 2

TOPS

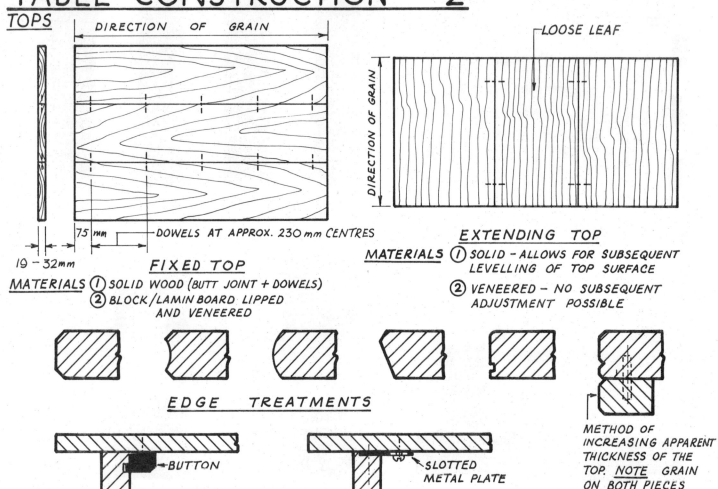

DIRECTION OF GRAIN

19 - 32mm

75 mm

— DOWELS AT APPROX. 230 mm CENTRES

FIXED TOP

MATERIALS ① SOLID WOOD (BUTT JOINT + DOWELS)
② BLOCK/LAMIN BOARD LIPPED
AND VENEERED

—LOOSE LEAF

DIRECTION OF GRAIN

EXTENDING TOP

MATERIALS ① SOLID - ALLOWS FOR SUBSEQUENT
LEVELLING OF TOP SURFACE
② VENEERED - NO SUBSEQUENT
ADJUSTMENT POSSIBLE

EDGE TREATMENTS

METHOD OF
INCREASING APPARENT
THICKNESS OF THE
TOP. NOTE GRAIN
ON BOTH PIECES
MUST BE IN THE
SAME DIRECTION

—BUTTON

—SLOTTED
METAL PLATE

METHODS OF FIXING TOPS TO RAILS

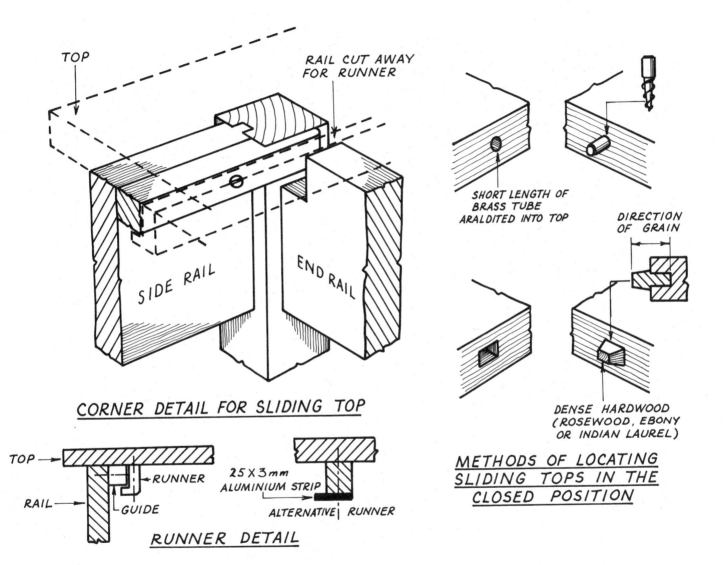

TOP

RAIL CUT AWAY
FOR RUNNER

SIDE RAIL

END RAIL

CORNER DETAIL FOR SLIDING TOP

TOP →

RAIL →

RUNNER

GUIDE

25 × 3 mm
ALUMINIUM STRIP

ALTERNATIVE RUNNER

RUNNER DETAIL

SHORT LENGTH OF
BRASS TUBE
ARALDITED INTO TOP

DIRECTION
OF GRAIN

DENSE HARDWOOD
(ROSEWOOD, EBONY
OR INDIAN LAUREL)

METHODS OF LOCATING
SLIDING TOPS IN THE
CLOSED POSITION

TABLE CONSTRUCTION—3

CONSTRUCTION REQUIRED WHEN A DRAWER IS INCLUDED IN THE DESIGN

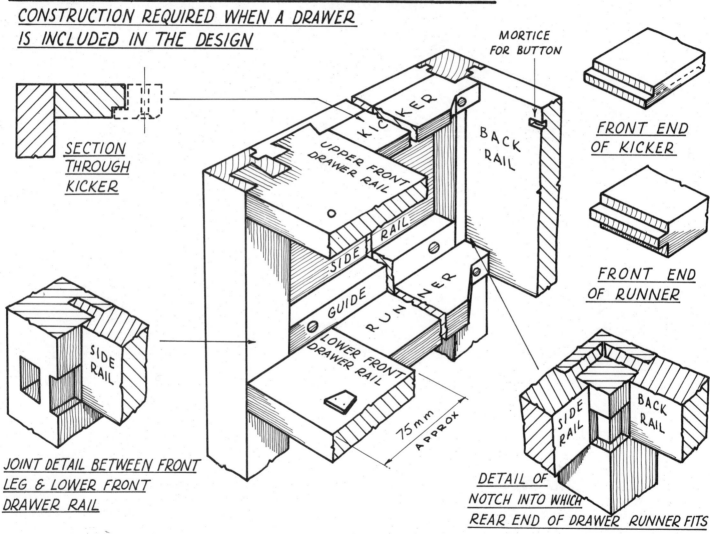

SECTION THROUGH KICKER

MORTICE FOR BUTTON

KICKER

BACK RAIL

UPPER FRONT DRAWER RAIL

SIDE RAIL

GUIDE

RUNNER

LOWER FRONT DRAWER RAIL

75 mm APPROX

FRONT END OF KICKER

FRONT END OF RUNNER

SIDE RAIL

JOINT DETAIL BETWEEN FRONT LEG & LOWER FRONT DRAWER RAIL

SIDE RAIL

BACK RAIL

DETAIL OF NOTCH INTO WHICH REAR END OF DRAWER RUNNER FITS

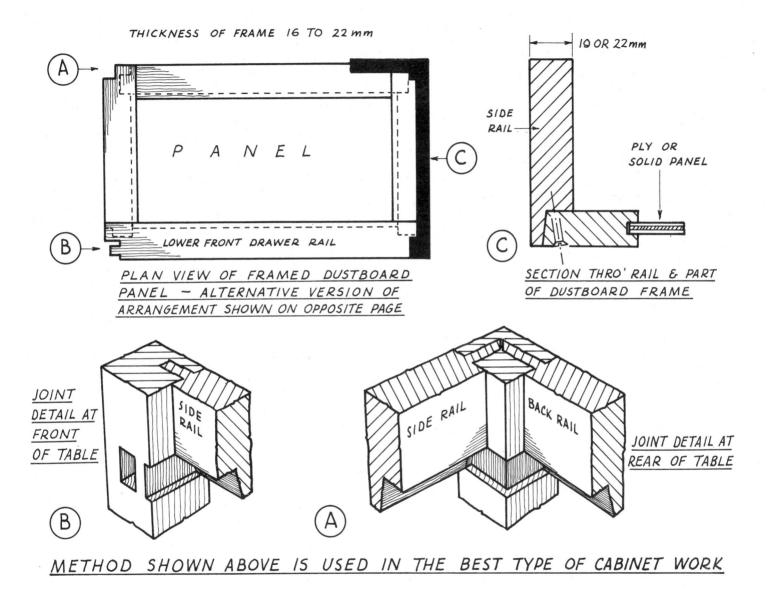

THICKNESS OF FRAME 16 TO 22 mm

(A)

P A N E L

LOWER FRONT DRAWER RAIL

(B)

(C)

PLAN VIEW OF FRAMED DUSTBOARD
PANEL — ALTERNATIVE VERSION OF
ARRANGEMENT SHOWN ON OPPOSITE PAGE

19 OR 22mm

SIDE
RAIL

PLY OR
SOLID PANEL

(C)

SECTION THRO' RAIL & PART
OF DUSTBOARD FRAME

JOINT
DETAIL AT
FRONT
OF TABLE

SIDE
RAIL

(B)

SIDE RAIL   BACK RAIL

JOINT DETAIL AT
REAR OF TABLE

(A)

METHOD SHOWN ABOVE IS USED IN THE BEST TYPE OF CABINET WORK

TABLE CONSTRUCTION–4

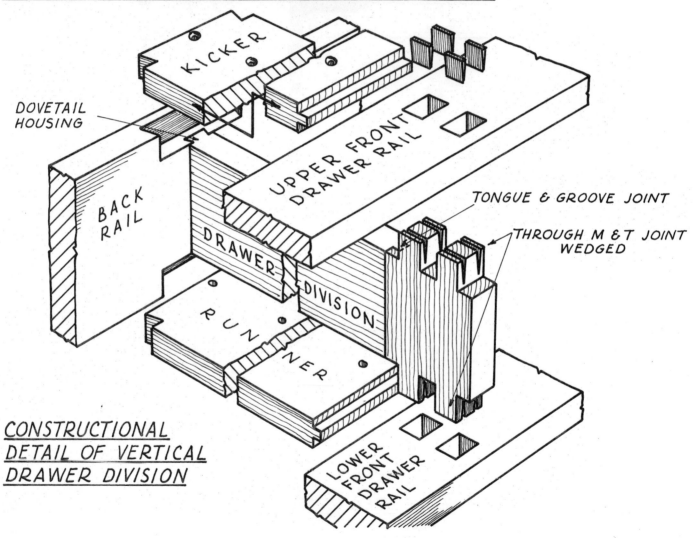

KICKER

DOVETAIL HOUSING

BACK RAIL

UPPER FRONT DRAWER RAIL

DRAWER

DIVISION

RUNNER

TONGUE & GROOVE JOINT

THROUGH M & T JOINT WEDGED

LOWER FRONT DRAWER RAIL

CONSTRUCTIONAL DETAIL OF VERTICAL DRAWER DIVISION

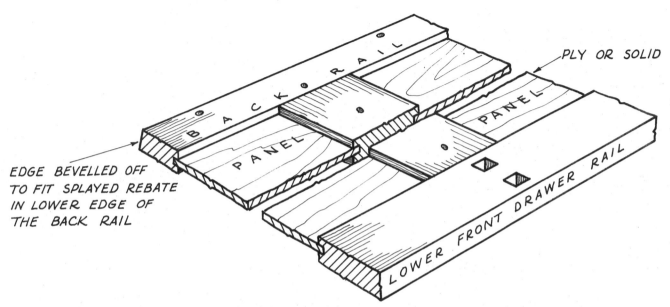

PLY OR SOLID

B A C K   R A I L

P A N E L

P A N E L

LOWER FRONT DRAWER RAIL

EDGE BEVELLED OFF
TO FIT SPLAYED REBATE
IN LOWER EDGE OF
THE BACK RAIL

DUSTBOARD PANEL – ALTERNATIVE DETAIL FOR UNDERNEATH CONSTRUCTION SHOWN ON THE OPPOSITE PAGE

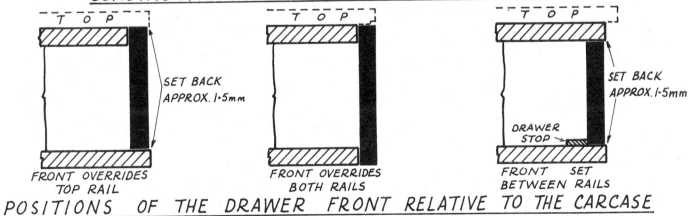

T O P

SET BACK
APPROX. 1·5mm

FRONT OVERRIDES
TOP RAIL

T O P

FRONT OVERRIDES
BOTH RAILS

T O P

SET BACK
APPROX. 1·5mm

DRAWER
STOP

FRONT   SET
BETWEEN RAILS

POSITIONS OF THE DRAWER FRONT RELATIVE TO THE CARCASE

STOOLS

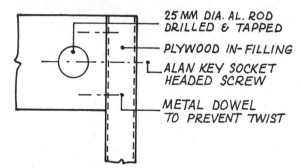

25 MM DIA. AL. ROD DRILLED & TAPPED

PLYWOOD IN-FILLING

ALAN KEY SOCKET HEADED SCREW

METAL DOWEL TO PREVENT TWIST

RAIL-LEG DETAIL

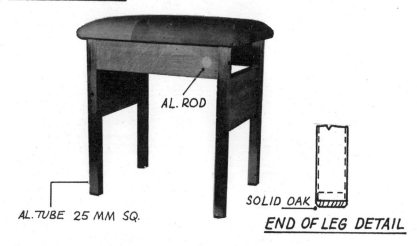

AL. ROD

AL. TUBE 25 MM SQ.

SOLID OAK

END OF LEG DETAIL

KNOCK-DOWN DRESSING TABLE STOOL
BY J. MAYNARD IN OAK & ALUMINIUM

FRAME BASED STOOL
BY J. A. FOWLES IN UTILE THIS IS A VERY SIMPLE SOLUTION TO THE PROBLEM USING BASIC CONSTRUCTIONAL TECHNIQUES

TABLES

REVOLVING GREEN SLATE CENTRE PIECE

VENEERED LAMINBOARD

AL. STRIP INLAY

SOLID TEAK

① **DINING TABLE** BY S. MOTHERSHAW IN TEAK WITH A SLATE CENTRE PIECE MOUNTED ON A TAPER ROLLER BEARING

② **REFECTORY TYPE TABLE** BY M. BELL IN COLUMBIAN PINE

SOLID PINE WITH THICKENED EDGES

THE PROBLEM
DESIGN A WORKING SURFACE SUITABLE FOR EATING FOR UP TO EIGHT PERSONS

PLY RAILS LIPPED & VENEERED

VENEERED LAMINBOARD

AL. LEG

③ **FOLDING LEAF EXTENDING TABLE** BY B. PAYNE IN AMERICAN BLACK WALNUT & ALUMINIUM LEGS

THE PHOTOGRAPHS SHOW THREE SOLUTIONS TO THE PROBLEM AT THE SCALE MODEL STAGE. THIS IS A VITAL PART OF THE DESIGN PROCESS WHEN A THREE DIMENSIONAL VIEW CAN BE OBTAINED OF THE INTENDED ARTEFACT AND CHANGES MAY BE CONSIDERED BEFORE THE JOB IS COMMITTED TO THE DRAWING BOARD

SHAPING — 1   LAMINATING USING VACUUM FORMING

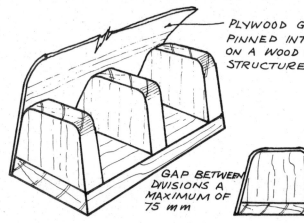

PLYWOOD GLUED AND
PINNED INTO POSITION
ON A WOOD OR CHIPBOARD
STRUCTURE

GAP BETWEEN
DIVISIONS A
MAXIMUM OF
75 mm

VACUUM FORMING THIS METHOD ENABLES
SHAPES TO BE MADE USING ONE FORMER ONLY.
CURVES CAN BE ACHIEVED DEPENDING UPON
THE MATERIALS BEING USED — MINIMUM
RADIUS IS 19 mm

SOLID WOOD OR
RIGID POLYURETHANE
FOAM

MATERIALS FORMERS   THESE CAN BE MADE FROM CHIPBOARD AND CONSTRUCTIONAL PLYWOOD (1·5 AND 3 mm)
SOLID WOOD OR RIGID POLYURETHANE FOAM BLOCKS WHICH CAN BE SHAPED
WITH SURFORMS ETC.

REQUIRED SHAPE — CORE OR CONSTRUCTIONAL VENEERS (NOT SUITABLE FOR SMALL RADII
AND ALSO TEND TO TWIST ALONG THE LENGTH)
CONSTRUCTIONAL PLYWOOD — ·8 mm, 1·5 mm, 3 mm, 4 mm (MAX) THIS MATERIAL
ALLOWS CURVES OF VARYING RADII TO BE FORMED WITHOUT THE HAZARD OF
SURFACE SPLITS UNDER PRESSURE

ADHESIVES — ANY ADHESIVE THAT ALLOWS A WORKING TIME FOR PLACING
IN THE ENVELOPE AND TOTAL EVACUATION

OTHER NEEDS — POLYTHENE SHEET — SELLOTAPE 25 mm WIDE.

VENEERS OR PLYWOOD LAYERS
MUST BE CUT 25 mm SMALLER
IN LENGTH AND TOTAL
WIDTH THAN
THE FORMER

WHEN TRIMMING
HAS TAKEN PLACE
THE REQUIRED
DIMENSIONS MUST
BE ACHIEVED

WASTE

VENEERS
NEED TO BE
ALTERNATED IN
GRAIN DIRECTION
TO GIVE STRENGTH TO
THE FORM

EXAMPLE OF VACUUM FORMING A SELECTED SHAPE

(AS FOR SOLUTION TO PROBLEM ON PAGE 16)

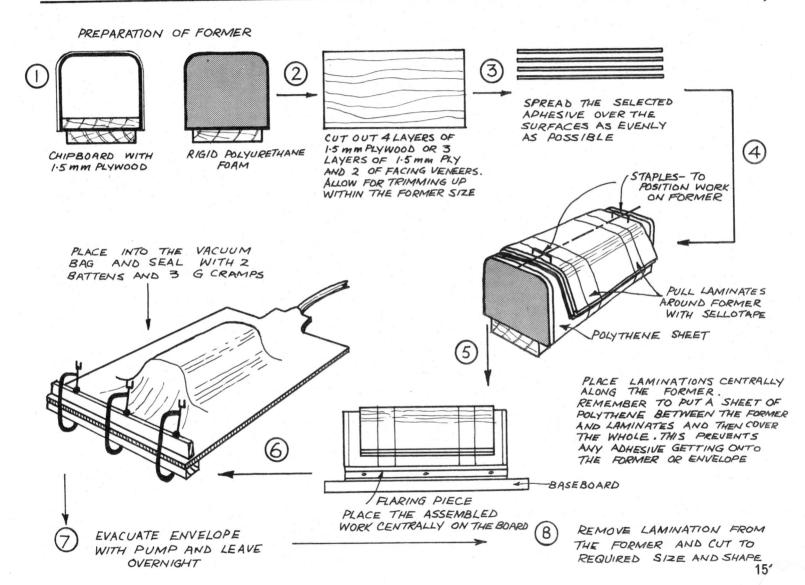

PREPARATION OF FORMER

① CHIPBOARD WITH 1·5 mm PLYWOOD

RIGID POLYURETHANE FOAM

② CUT OUT 4 LAYERS OF 1·5 mm PLYWOOD OR 3 LAYERS OF 1·5 mm PLY AND 2 OF FACING VENEERS. ALLOW FOR TRIMMING UP WITHIN THE FORMER SIZE

③ SPREAD THE SELECTED ADHESIVE OVER THE SURFACES AS EVENLY AS POSSIBLE

④

STAPLES- TO POSITION WORK ON FORMER

PULL LAMINATES AROUND FORMER WITH SELLOTAPE

POLYTHENE SHEET

⑤ PLACE LAMINATIONS CENTRALLY ALONG THE FORMER. REMEMBER TO PUT A SHEET OF POLYTHENE BETWEEN THE FORMER AND LAMINATES AND THEN COVER THE WHOLE. THIS PREVENTS ANY ADHESIVE GETTING ONTO THE FORMER OR ENVELOPE

PLACE INTO THE VACUUM BAG AND SEAL WITH 2 BATTENS AND 3 G CRAMPS

⑥ FLARING PIECE PLACE THE ASSEMBLED WORK CENTRALLY ON THE BOARD

BASEBOARD

⑦ EVACUATE ENVELOPE WITH PUMP AND LEAVE OVERNIGHT

⑧ REMOVE LAMINATION FROM THE FORMER AND CUT TO REQUIRED SIZE AND SHAPE

15'

SHAPING—2   OTHER CURVES AND FORMERS

WHEN PREPARING FORMERS FOR VACUUM FORMING ON A BASEBOARD IT IS IMPORTANT TO ENSURE THAT NO AIR POCKETS OCCUR IN THE WORK. ALL FORMERS SHOULD HAVE FLARING PIECES THINNER THAN THE SUPPORTING BOARD. WITHOUT THESE FLARINGS THE ENVELOPE WILL PUSH THE LAMINATES AWAY FROM THE FORMER CAUSING AIR POCKETS AND MISSHAPES.

OR

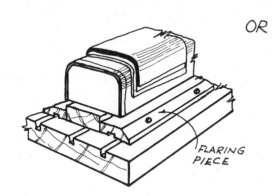

FLARING PIECE

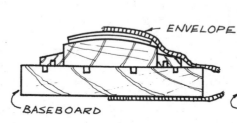

ENVELOPE

BASEBOARD

OR

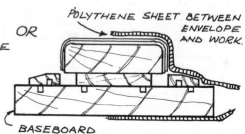

POLYTHENE SHEET BETWEEN ENVELOPE AND WORK.

BASEBOARD

ESSENTIALS

1. WELL PREPARED FORMER
2. EXACT TAILORING OF LAMINATES AND VENEERS
3. CORRECTLY DESIGNED FLARING PIECES
4. CORRECT GLUE MIX
5. CORRECT GLUE SPREAD
6. COVERING OF SURFACES WITH POLYTHENE SHEET TO PROTECT ENVELOPE AND FORMER FROM GLUE
7. ADEQUATE PRESSURE AND TIME UNDER PRESSURE OVER THE WHOLE AREA

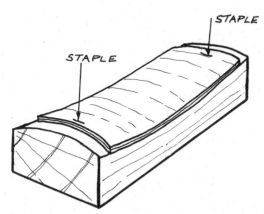

STAPLE

STAPLE

WHEN FORMING A SHALLOW COMPOUND CURVE NO BASEBOARD IS REQUIRED THIS WILL ALLOW THE ENVELOPE TO PULL ALL ROUND THE WORK. COVER THE SURFACE OF THE FACE VENEER WITH GUMMED TAPE TO AVOID SPLITTING

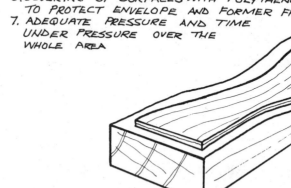
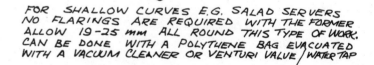

FOR SHALLOW CURVES E.G. SALAD SERVERS NO FLARINGS ARE REQUIRED WITH THE FORMER ALLOW 19-25 mm ALL ROUND THIS TYPE OF WORK. CAN BE DONE WITH A POLYTHENE BAG EVACUATED WITH A VACUUM CLEANER OR VENTURI VALVE / WATER TAP

SHAPED BACK RAIL
3 LAYERS OF 5 MM PLY
VENEERED ON BOTH FACES
& LIPPED ON BOTH EDGES

SHAPED SEAT RAIL
3 LAYERS OF 5 MM PLY
VENEERED ON BOTH FACES
& LIPPED ON LOWER EDGE
ONLY

<u>DINING CHAIR</u> BY J. MAYNARD
IN TEAK

BACK RAIL MOULD

SEAT RAIL MOULD

BASEBOARD COVERED
WITH POLYTHENE SHEET

POLYTHENE SHEET ON
BOTH FACES OF MOULD
TO PREVENT ADHESION

DEAL MOULDS USED FOR SHAPING —
THE INNER FACES COVERED WITH CARD

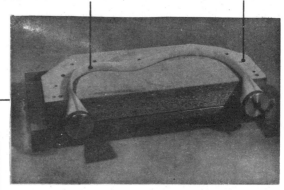

ARMOURED FIRE HOSE   CHIPBOARD MOULD

AN ALTERNATIVE METHOD OF PRODUCING
CURVED LAMINAE USING ARMOURED
FIRE HOSE AT 30 LBS PER SQ. IN.
PRESSURE
JIGS DESIGNED & MADE BY L. OUSELEY

GUIDE DOWELS

A MOULD MADE FROM BLOCKBOARD
USED TO PRODUCE A SIMPLE CURVED
SHAPE WHICH CAN BE USED TO FORM
THE BASIS OF A NUMBER OF USEFUL
CONSTRUCTIONAL UNITS SIMILAR TO
THE ONE SHOWN ABOVE

SHAPING—3 FORMING A BRACELET

THIS METHOD CONSISTS OF USING A SPLIT FORMER, "PIRELLI" WEBBING
AND THE REQUIRED LAMINATES E.G. FACE AND CORE VENEERS

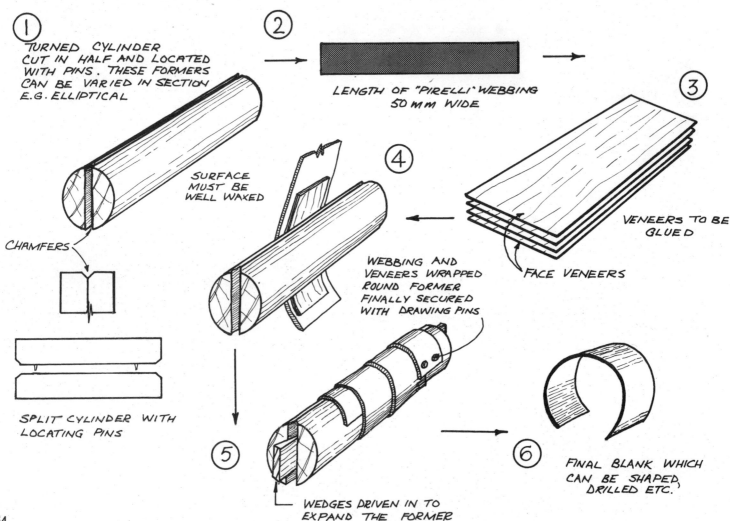

① TURNED CYLINDER
CUT IN HALF AND LOCATED
WITH PINS. THESE FORMERS
CAN BE VARIED IN SECTION
E.G. ELLIPTICAL

SURFACE
MUST BE
WELL WAXED

CHAMFERS

SPLIT CYLINDER WITH
LOCATING PINS

② LENGTH OF "PIRELLI" WEBBING
50 mm WIDE

③ VENEERS TO BE
GLUED

FACE VENEERS

④ WEBBING AND
VENEERS WRAPPED
ROUND FORMER
FINALLY SECURED
WITH DRAWING PINS

⑤ WEDGES DRIVEN IN TO
EXPAND THE FORMER

⑥ FINAL BLANK WHICH
CAN BE SHAPED
DRILLED ETC.

154

LAMINATING BY MALE AND FEMALE FORMERS

LAMINATED SHAPES CAN BE ACHIEVED BY THE USE OF A TWO PART FORMER WITH PRESSURE APPLIED USING A VICE OR CRAMPS
IT IS IMPORTANT TO NOTE THE FOLLOWING TO ACHIEVE GOOD RESULTS

<u>PRESSURE</u> MUST BE APPLIED AT <u>ALL</u> POINTS OF THE FORMERS

<u>TYPE OF FORMER</u>

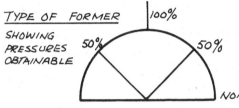

SHOWING PRESSURES OBTAINABLE

100%
50%   50%
NON-EXISTENT

NOT MORE THAN A QUADRANT FOR A MALE AND FEMALE FORMER

IF THE MALE FORMER IS MORE THAN A QUADRANT SEGMENTED FEMALE FORMERS FROM THE CENTRE MUST BE USED

<u>SUCCESS</u> IS DEPENDENT UPON THE WORK FLOWING — THE ENDS MUST NOT BE TRAPPED

<u>LAMINA THICKNESS</u>   THIS SHOULD BE KEPT DOWN TO A MINIMUM IN ORDER TO NEGOTIATE THE TIGHTEST CURVE USED

EXAMPLES OF FORMERS

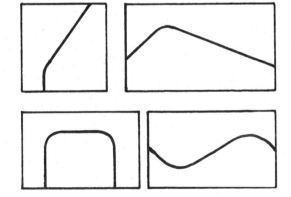

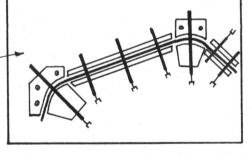

BASEBOARD COVERED WITH POLYTHENE

USE POLYTHENE STRIPS BETWEEN LAMINATES AND FORMERS TO PREVENT GLUE STICKING TO THEM

THIS METHOD INVOLVES A BASEBOARD WITH SOME FORMERS FIXED IN POSITION — OTHERS ARE LOOSE AND POSITIONED WITH G CRAMPS
IN THIS WAY LARGE FORMS CAN BE CONSTRUCTED E.G. CHAIRS, ETC.

MATERIALS
FACE VENEERS: CORE/CONSTRUCTIONAL VENEERS: THIN STRIPS OF WOOD(ASH) : MM PLYWOOD (VERY SUITABLE) STRIPS OF SOLID TIMBER MUST BE STRAIGHT GRAINED

SCULPTURE — 1

SCULPTURE IS BEST CONCEIVED WHEN NATURAL FORMS E.G. BONES, PEBBLES, ETC. ARE USED AS A SOURCE OF IDEAS.
FROM THESE FORMS SHAPES CAN BE DEVELOPED USING A VARIETY OF TOOLS AND MATERIALS THE FORM IS THEN WORKED IN THE WOOD TAKING FULL ADVANTAGE OF ITS GRAIN, PATTERN, COLOUR RANGE ETC.

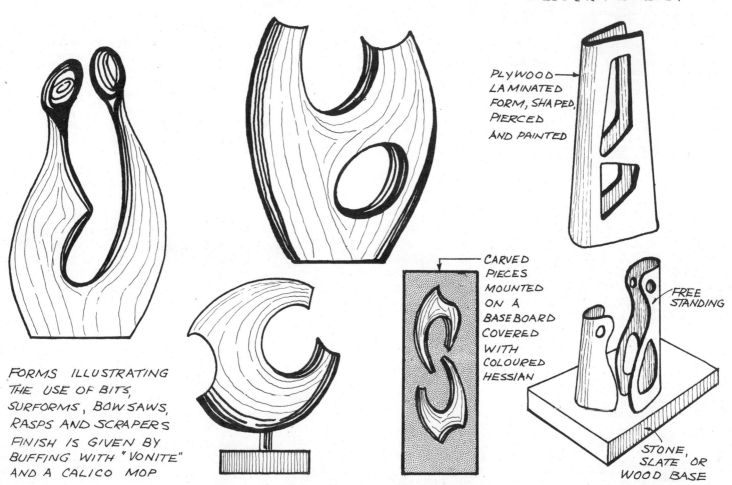

PLYWOOD LAMINATED FORM, SHAPED, PIERCED AND PAINTED

CARVED PIECES MOUNTED ON A BASEBOARD COVERED WITH COLOURED HESSIAN

FREE STANDING

STONE, SLATE OR WOOD BASE

FORMS ILLUSTRATING THE USE OF BITS, SURFORMS, BOW SAWS, RASPS AND SCRAPERS
FINISH IS GIVEN BY BUFFING WITH "VONITE" AND A CALICO MOP

FORMS

THIS TYPE OF WORK MAKES GOOD USE OF 19MM MATERIAL.
THEMES CAN BE CHOSEN E.G. FISH, ANIMALS, BIRDS, FACES ETC.
   USING FORSTNER BITS, DRILLS, COPING SAWS, RASPS, ETC., THE INDIVIDUAL
PIECES ARE SHAPED. COLOUR AND TEXTURE CAN BE APPLIED BY USING ACRYLIC
PAINTS AND SCRAP MATERIAL— VINYL, CORD, LEATHER, FABRICS, ETC.

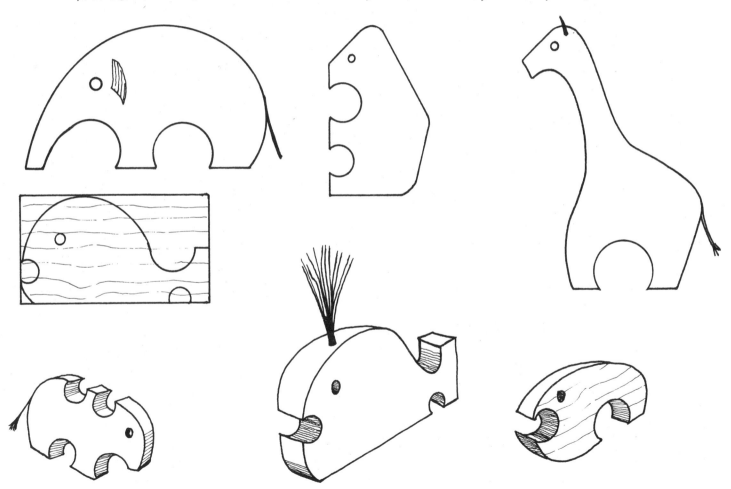

SCULPTURE—2 USING BASIC TOOL TECHNIQUES

MARKING OUT, SAWING, CHISELLING, BORING, PLANING, ABRADING.
USE OF COLOUR — ACRYLIC PAINTS, COLOURED PERSPEX, RESINS, MM PLYWOODS

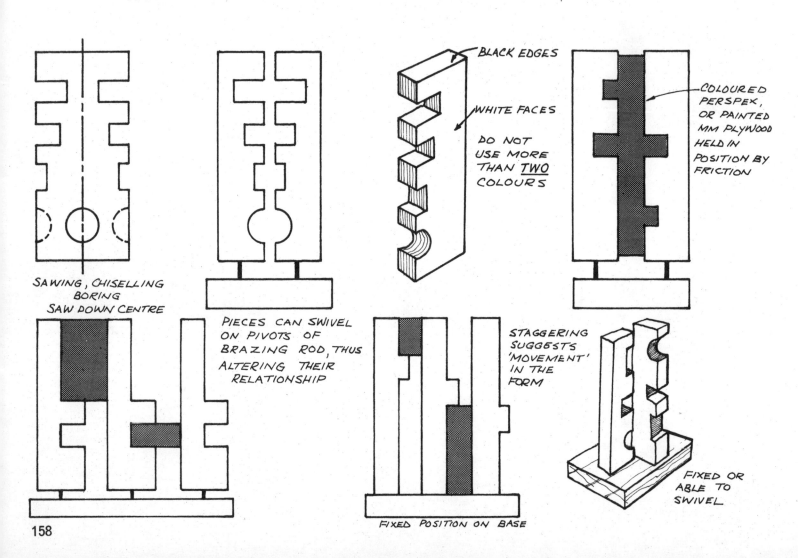

SAWING, CHISELLING
BORING
SAW DOWN CENTRE

PIECES CAN SWIVEL
ON PIVOTS OF
BRAZING ROD, THUS
ALTERING THEIR
RELATIONSHIP

BLACK EDGES

WHITE FACES

DO NOT
USE MORE
THAN TWO
COLOURS

COLOURED
PERSPEX,
OR PAINTED
MM PLYWOOD
HELD IN
POSITION BY
FRICTION

STAGGERING
SUGGESTS
'MOVEMENT'
IN THE
FORM

FIXED POSITION ON BASE

FIXED OR
ABLE TO
SWIVEL

EXAMPLES OF SCULPTURAL FORMS USING PLOUGHED GROOVES, DOWEL ROD, PERSPEX, ETC.

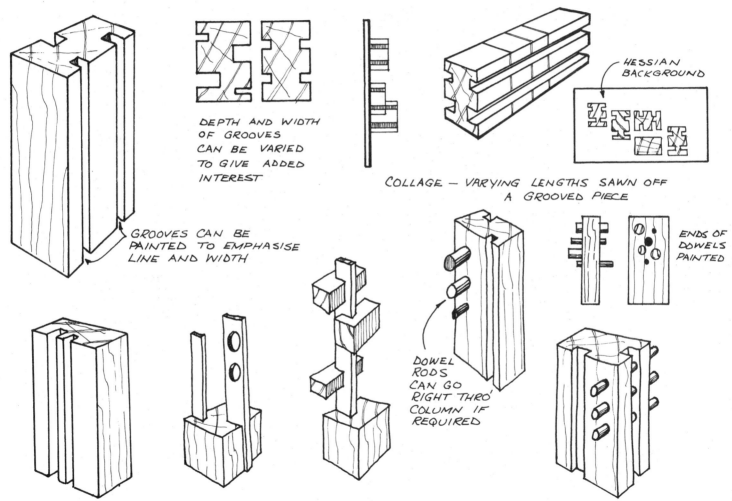

DEPTH AND WIDTH OF GROOVES CAN BE VARIED TO GIVE ADDED INTEREST

HESSIAN BACKGROUND

COLLAGE — VARYING LENGTHS SAWN OFF A GROOVED PIECE

GROOVES CAN BE PAINTED TO EMPHASISE LINE AND WIDTH

ENDS OF DOWELS PAINTED

DOWEL RODS CAN GO RIGHT THRO' COLUMN IF REQUIRED

SCULPTURAL FORMS

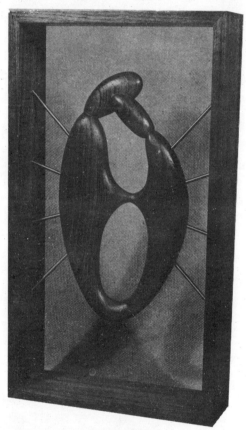

SCULPTURAL FORMS

DESIGNED AND MADE BY A. ALCOCK.

AND D. WEBSTER.

'MOTHER & CHILD'
IN TEAK

'GEOMETRICAL FORM'
IN UTILE

INDEX

© 1975 J. MAYNARD
       D. A. JONES
First published 1966 by Hulton Educational Publications Ltd., Raans Road, Amersham, Bucks.
Revised and metricated 1975.
Reprinted 1981 in GDR by Interdruck, Leipzig
Filmset and printed in Great Britain by BAS Printers Limited, Wallop, Hampshire.
ISBN 0 7175 0696 7